Vintage Automobiles Vol.1

Set in Scotch Roman, and on an electric keyboard,
and printed by the
YEOVIL PRINTING COMPANY
South Western Terrace, Yeovil, Somerset

Vintage Automobiles Vol.1

Technical Descriptions and Illustrations - Maintenance and Repair

by H. Thornton Rutter

PUBLISHED BY

J H HAYNES & CO. LTD., 44 OLD BOND STREET,

LONDON, W.1.

COUNTY LIBRARY
~~629.2222~~
~~629.288~~
4515634
629.222

CONTENTS

INTRODUCTION

This is the first volume of a new series of books concerned solely with the vintage automobile. Each of the three volumes will comprise a carefully made and interesting selection of reprints from H. Thornton Rutter's now very rare, five volume work, 'Motors of Today', which was originally published circa 1928.

The information in these following pages is detailed and highly specialised and makes fascinating reading to those with a genuine and deep interest in vintage automobiles. This is not a book which will appeal to those that are only casually interested in the cars of the 20's, but the true enthusiast will find much to delight and absorb him.

The cost, secondhand, of the original five volume work, when copies can be found, amounts to at least £25. It is hoped, by making a careful selection of models from the original work, to give enthusiasts three volumes which cover all the more interesting and important makes at a fraction of this cost. At the same time we have made every endeavour to keep the price down and the quality up. It has not been possible to renumber the illustrations, and references to them, and the original page numbers in the text, however we hope this will not cause any inconvenience.

We would like to particularly thank Mr. G. Virtue of Virtue and Co. Ltd., the original publishers of 'Motors of Today', for his kindness in allowing us to use their copyright matter. Where reproduction of some of the pages is not all that it might be we would like readers to know that this is entirely due to the deterioration of the original volumes over the years and not due to the original printing.

ALFA-ROMEO

$1\frac{1}{2}$-LITRE AND 3-LITRE MOULDS

As one of the firms who have been winners of Grand Prix races, Alfa-Romeo cars, built in Italy by the Societa Anonima Italiana Ingenieur Nicola Romeo & Company, of Milan, find their place in England due to their sporting type. Two models, outside the purely racing machines, are to be found on British roads, viz., the six-cylinder 15-60 H.P. with a bore of 62 mm. and a stroke of 82, made in two types, the ordinary touring and the sports; the 22-70 H.P. model with six cylinders of 76 bore by 110 stroke and, like the smaller Alfa-Romeo, also having a touring and a sports engine as its companion. The chassis are all somewhat similar.

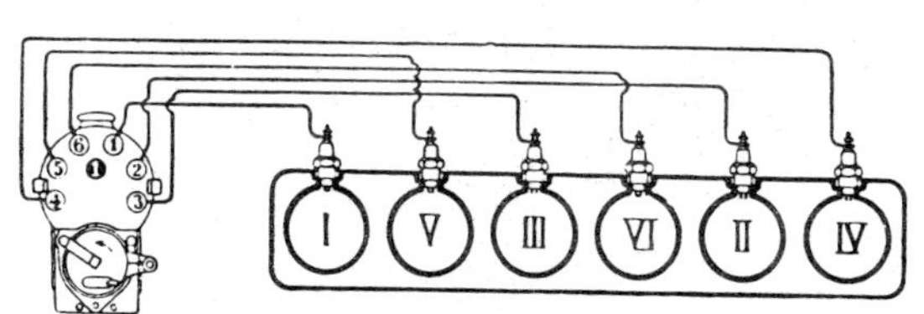

FIG. 72.—Order of Firing (No. 1 cylinder nearest to radiator).

The six-cylinder 1,487 c.c. has overhead valves actuated by an overhead camshaft supported on five main bearings. The ignition is by coil and battery, but so arranged that should the battery fail, current can be supplied direct to the sparking plugs by the dynamo. The water cooling is by a centrifugal pump, aided by a fan driven directly by the camshaft, while the lubrication of the engine is a forced feed system by gear-driven pump. A Solex carburettor with hot air intake and adjustable fresh air port is provided on the touring car ; but for the sports models two Zenith carburettors

Fig. 73.—Twin Zenith Carburettors on Super-Sports Type.
R. Air regulator.

Fig. 74.—Valve Adjustment.

are fitted, similar to those fitted to the larger 22-90 H.P. six-cylinder model, the sports edition of the 22-70 H.P. touring type. On this 15 H.P. rated six-cylinder Alfa-Romeo, the carburettor is supplied with its fuel by gravity, the petrol tank being mounted on the dashboard. The other details of its construction include a multiple disc clutch with ferrobestos linings, a four-speed forward gear-box with controls by central lever, cardan shaft with one universal joint and central strutting tube, straight springs, a pressed rear axle, front and rear self-adjustable shock absorbers, four-wheel brake controls by pedal and hand lever, placed in the centre of the car. A 12-volt lighting set and electrical starter, straight-sided wire wheels with 30 × 5·25 in. tyres for the long wheel base model and 28 × 4·95 in. tyres for the short or sports model are included.

The 22-70 H.P. Alfa-Romeo has a total cubic capacity in the engine of 2,994 c.c. and is rated at 22 H.P. It has also overhead valves with push-rods and rocker arms actuated by a camshaft enclosed in the engine base chamber. The ignition, however, is by magneto, and the carburettor a Solex with adjustable hot air intake and a device for closing the fresh air port when the engine is first started up. It also has a mixture-warming device. Like the smaller model, the petrol supply is also by the vacuum system used to draw the supply from the main tank in the rear to the autovac carried on the dashboard. A dry plate clutch is common to all these models. The four wheel brakes on this model are controlled by the pedal only, as the hand brake operates on the transmission, the brake drum being placed behind the gear-box. In the sports model the lubrication is a forced feed system by a gear-driven pump, sucking the oil from a tank under the dashboard, while a second pump sucks the oil which collects in the engine base chamber and returns it to this tank.

The order of firing of the cylinders in all of these models is similar, viz., 1, 5, 3, 6, 2, and 4, No. 1 cylinder being that nearest to the radiator (Fig. 72). The touring models are timed as follows :—

Inlet valve opens at 5° before top dead centre and closes 50° after bottom dead centre.

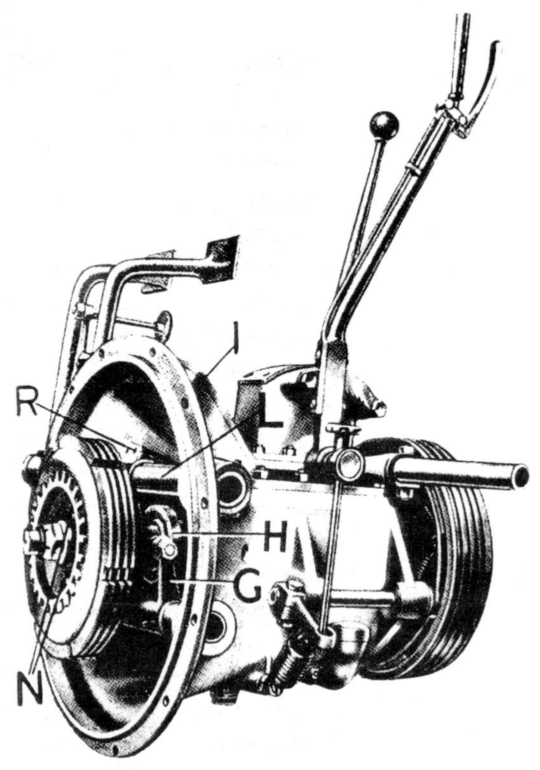

Fig. 75.—Clutch and Gear-Box.

G, Clutch lever. I, Casing. R, Lever.
H, Bearing. L, Pedal tube. N, Nuts for adjusting clutch.

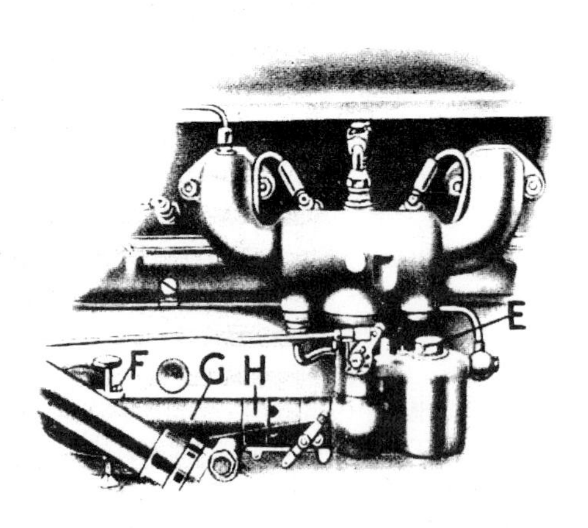

Fig. 76.—Solex Carburettor of Touring Car.

E, Front chamber. F, Hot air control. G, Induction tube. H, Cold air inlet.

Exhaust valve opens 45° before B.D.C. and closes 10° after T.D.C. The fly-wheel is stamped with the figures 1-4 corresponding respectively to the top dead centres of Nos. 1 and 4 cylinders, and also marked with the figures 6-3 and 5-2, showing the T.D.C. respectively of those pairs of cylinders.

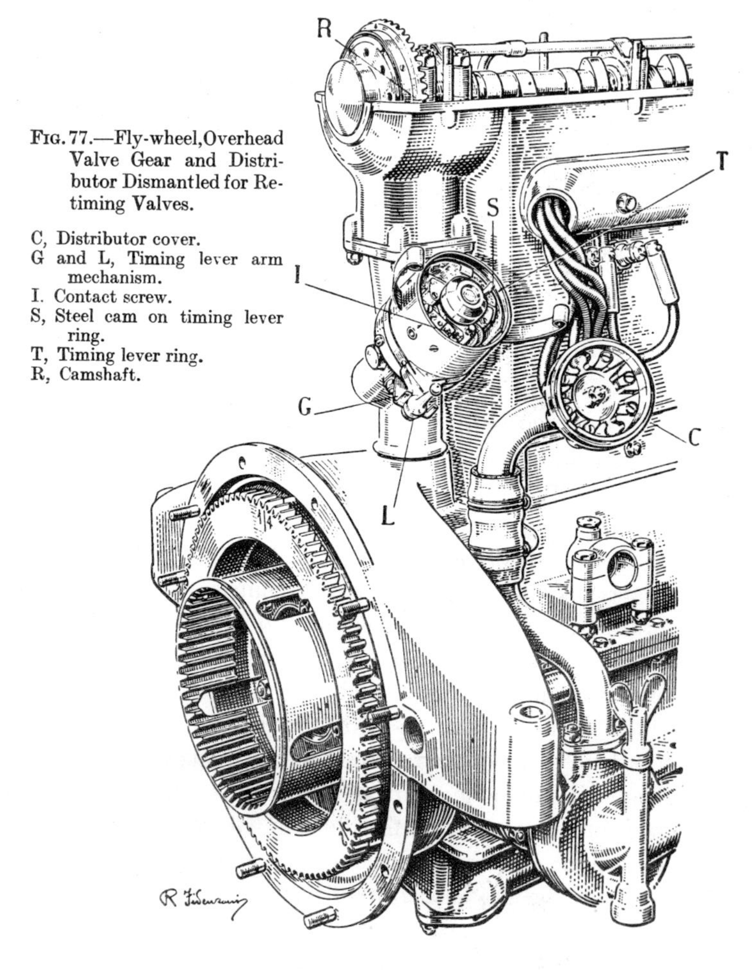

FIG. 77.—Fly-wheel, Overhead Valve Gear and Distributor Dismantled for Retiming Valves.

C, Distributor cover.
G and L, Timing lever arm mechanism.
I. Contact screw.
S, Steel cam on timing lever ring.
T, Timing lever ring.
R, Camshaft.

In the general lay-out the six-cylinder 1,500 c.c. Alfa-Romeo chassis is very similar to the larger 22-70 H.P. model. The timing is different, as the inlet valve opens 5° before T.D.C. and closes 53° after B.D.C., the exhaust valve opens at 45° before B.D.C. and closes 13° after T.D.C., the fly-wheel being marked similarly as in the model above described. The order of firing is also identical.

The following remarks, while they apply to the six-cylinder 22-70 H.P. model, are equally applicable to the $1\frac{1}{2}$-litre Alfa-Romeo.

Thus in summer the air ports of the carburettors should be fully open; the tension of the fan belt should be examined and if necessary adjusted by means of the nut provided. The belt should be rather taut, though not more than slightly so, in order not to overheat the front bearing of the camshaft. It should be remembered that the belt should only work on the sides of the pulley. Should the belt wear after long use

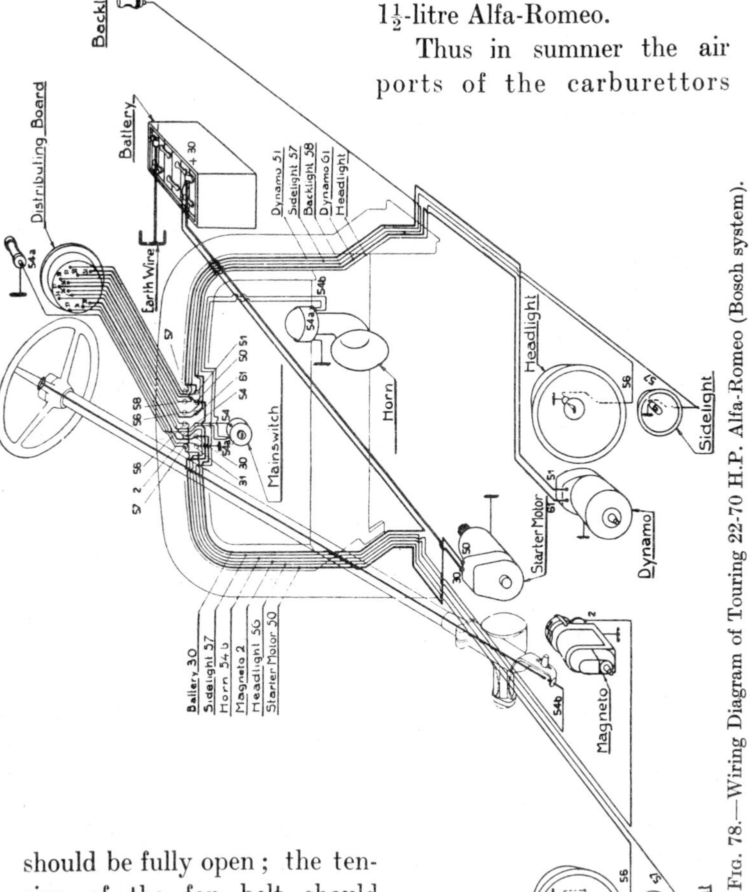

FIG. 78.—Wiring Diagram of Touring 22-70 H.P. Alfa-Romeo (Bosch system).

and appear to be driving on the bottom of the groove, it should immediately be replaced.

In winter the air ports of the carburettors should be closed. It may be necessary to partly blank off the lower portion of the radiator; also, possibly, it is necessary to remove the fan belt to prevent overcooling of the engine.

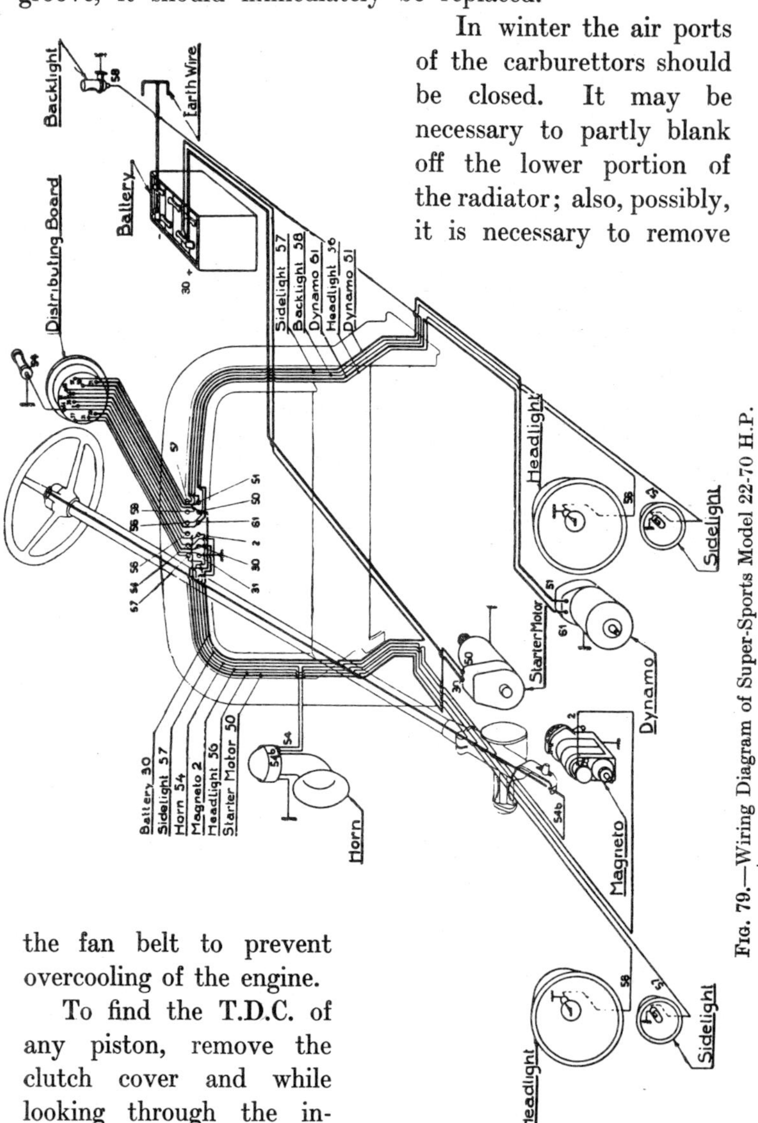

FIG. 79.—Wiring Diagram of Super-Sports Model 22-70 H.P.

To find the T.D.C. of any piston, remove the clutch cover and while looking through the inspection hole revolve the engine slowly by hand. The numbers becoming visible on the fly-wheel indicate the numbers of the cylinders in which the pistons are at T.D.C., either 1-4, or 6-3, or 5-2.

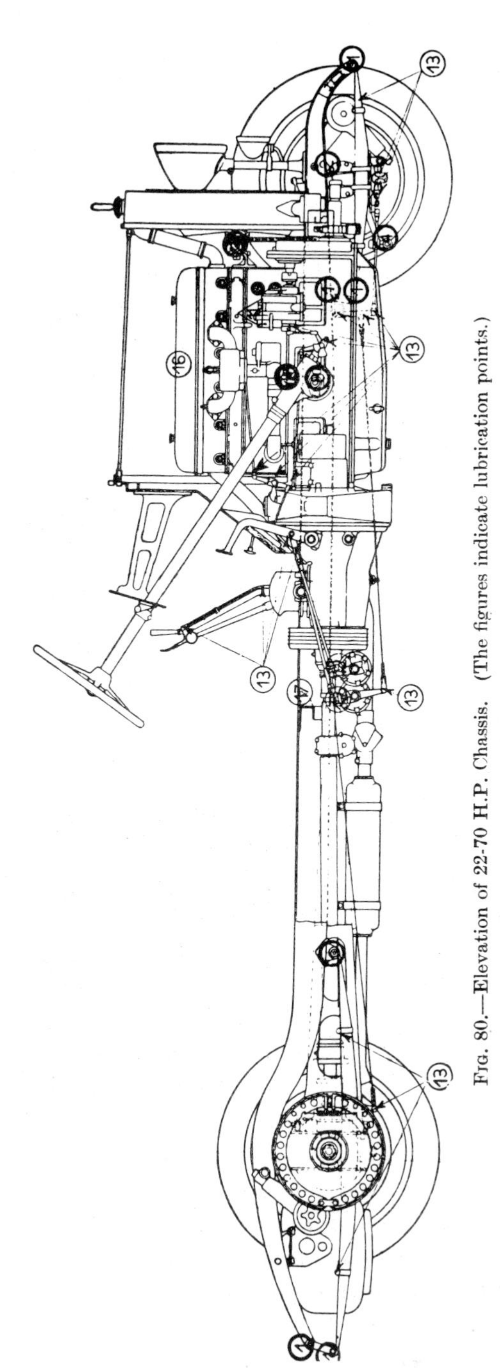

Fig. 80.—Elevation of 22-70 H.P. Chassis. (The figures indicate lubrication points.)

To time the camshaft, before dismounting either the crankshaft or the camshaft, mark two consecutive teeth on the gearing of the camshaft and also mark the tooth on the gearing of the crankshaft which engages between them. By doing this it will be easy later on to remount everything in the exact position as before. The first process when there is no available data is to proceed by revolving the crankshaft by hand until No. 1 piston is at T.D.C., next adjust the tappets of $\frac{12}{1000}$ in., then revolve the camshaft without mounting the camshaft gearing, therefore without connection with the crankshaft, until the inlet valve of No. 1 cylinder, which is the one nearest to the radiator, is on the point of opening. To make sure that this valve is on the point of opening, hold the cup of the springs between the fingers and try to turn the valve itself round. As long as the valve is closed it will be impossible to move it.

Great care should then be taken not to change the positions of either crank or cam shaft. The gears of the camshaft should then be mounted, and timing will thus be completed.

The compression may be checked by allowing the engine to run at low speed with the cut-out open. If the sound made by the exhaust of each cylinder is similar and equal there is no loss of compression as far as the engine is concerned. It is also possible to test the compression by turning the starting handle slowly so that the hand will feel the resistance offered by each cylinder. These resistances should be equal.

Should the compression not be correct, first look to the tappet adjustment. If there is the necessary play of $\frac{12}{1000}$ in. between the rocker arm levers and the tappet stems when the engine is slightly warm, and if there is no loss of gas from the sparking plug or through the packing between the cylinders and the cylinder head when the engine is running, the trouble is usually due to the valves, which are not fitting properly on their seats. The remedy, of course, is to regrind them.

To regrind the valves it is necessary to first empty the water from the radiator, free the cylinder head from the rocker arms, sparking plugs, inlet and exhaust pipes, water outlet, and finally from the stud bolts. When the head is free, dismantle it by raising it with four suitable tommy bars introduced into the inlet and exhaust ports. By proceeding in this manner the copper and asbestos packing between the head and the cylinder will not be damaged, as might happen if the head were removed by means of screw-drivers or other instruments used as levers and inserted under the head. Should, however, this gasket be damaged, it must be removed, the valves being freed by lowering the cups of the springs and by removing the stop-rings; if the surface is slightly corroded they should be ground in; if, however, seriously pitted, they may have to be turned up or a new valve procured.

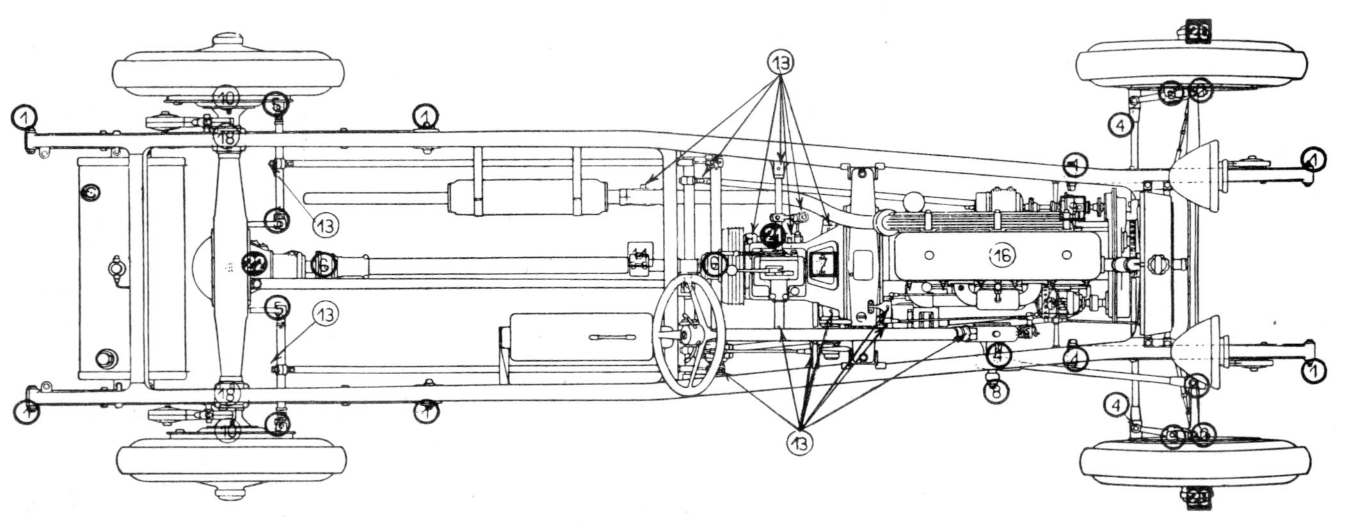

Fig. 81.—Plan of 22-70 H.P. Chassis. (The figures indicate lubrication points.)

Modern valve grinding in a workshop is now done by an electrical tool, which makes the work very simple, but those who prefer to do it by hand should rest the cylinder head on one side and use a suitable tool with which to handle the valve. Valve grinding is simplified by the employment of a light spiral spring placed between the head of the valve and the head of the cylinders, so that the valve will be automatically raised when not pressed against the head of the cylinders.

The actual operation is conducted by smearing the surface of the valve head with grinding paste and oil, then applying slight pressure, revolving the valve in alternate directions. The position of the valve in the seating should be changed every seven or eight turns and this operation repeated until a very highly polished surface is obtained. The valves, valve seatings and ports in the cylinder head should then be washed with paraffin so as to remove all traces of the grinding paste. When remounting, it must be remembered to grease thoroughly with a mixture of grease and paraffin, whilst great care must be exercised to see that each valve is replaced in its correct seating.

Fig. 74, p. 106, shows the method of adjusting the tappets. This is done when the engine is slightly warm, then by means of the starting handle revolve the crankshaft slowly until both valves of each cylinder in turn are closed. When in this position insert a thin sheet of metal or $\frac{12}{1000}$ in. feeler gauge and adjust until it is lightly gripped between the rocker arm lever and the tappet itself. If the tappet play is considerably more than $\frac{12}{1000}$ in., the engine will run very noisily. If instead it is less than $\frac{12}{1000}$ in. the valve will not close perfectly when the engine is warm, and a loss of power will ensue.

The Solex carburettor which is usually fitted on the touring models, as shown in Fig. 76, p. 108, is adjusted for petrol of a specific gravity of ·730, so that if fuel of a different density is used it may be necessary to adjust the carburettor accordingly. To facilitate carburation in cold weather the air inlet ports should be closed by means of the sleeve H, whereas they should be kept wide open in summer and warm weather. The Solex carburettor requires cleaning for the small filter, the float chamber, and the jets periodically. This can be accomplished by unscrewing the nut E when the entire lower portion of the carburettor can be detached. To separate the carburettor from the warm air inlet tube G, remove screw F, and move tube G slightly backwards.

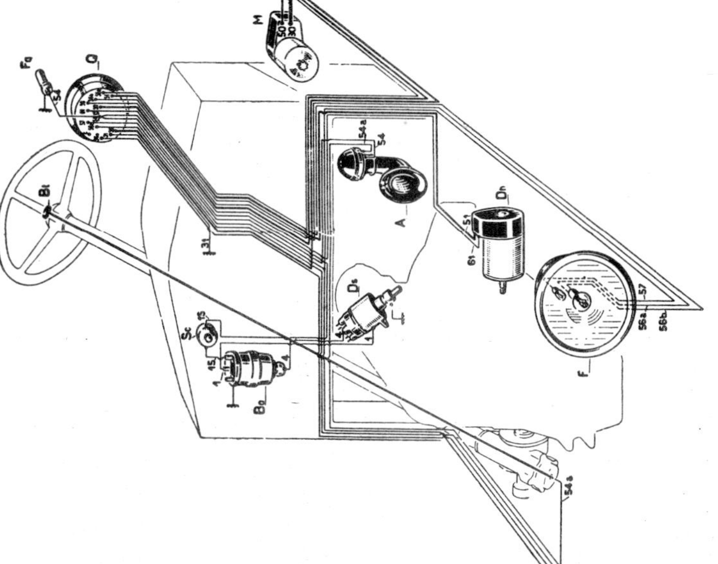

FIG. 82.—Wiring Diagram of 1½-litre Chassis (Bosch system).

The super-sports models are generally fitted with two vertical Zenith carburettors, as depicted in Fig. 73, p. 106, each of which is fitted with a warm air inlet from the tappet chamber and two adjustable cold air inlets. The mixture before entering the cylinders is further heated by means of warm water circulating in respective chambers cast in one piece with the induction pipes. Here again, to make starting easier, and to improve carburation in cold weather, the cold air inlet regulators R, Fig. 73, should be closed, whereas they should be kept wide open in summer and in warm weather.

The two hot water cocks above the carburettor should never be closed except when dismounting the induction pipe or the cylinder head.

The petrol tank at the rear of the car holds 16 gals. Care should be taken to see that the cap covering the filling orifice has its small hole kept clear to allow the free passage of air through it to the tank.

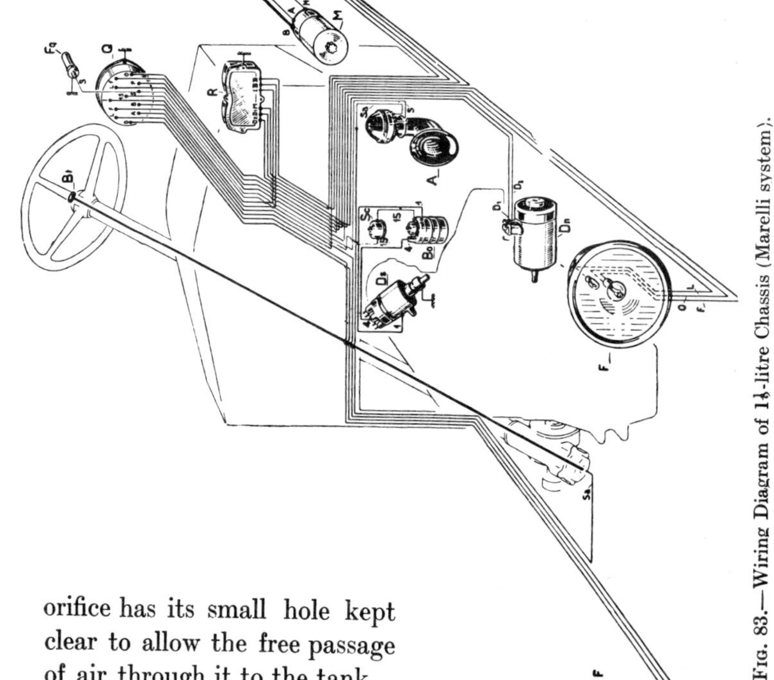

FIG. 83.—Wiring Diagram of 1½-litre Chassis (Marelli system).

On the super-sports models, on the contrary, the tank cap should be kept well closed, with no air leaks, as on that model the petrol is pressure-fed to the carburettor. An air pump or pulsometer is driven by the engine camshaft and thus maintains a pressure of about 3 lbs. to the square inch in the petrol tank, necessary to give a regular supply of fuel to the carburettors. In the super-sports models, also, a hand pump is provided to raise the pressure in the fuel tank when starting the engine from cold, and a gauge for indicating the pressure in the main tank is fitted to the dashboard.

In the case of insufficiency of pressure or constant failing of pressure, the tank cap, tube union, and air tube should be examined. Search should be made to find the point at which air can escape; the tube unions, and if necessary also the tubes themselves, should be covered with a film of oil in order that when pressure is put on by the hand pump the defective place or leak is discovered where bubbles may appear.

The lack of pressure may also be due to dirt having settled in the valve of the air pump and keeping it constantly open, therefore this valve should be taken down and cleaned, but when remounting, care should be taken not to alter its original adjustment.

The engine lubrication in the touring model is effected by pressure through a gear pump situated in the bottom of the sump. This pump sucks up the oil and sends it to the crankshaft bearings from where it is splashed in all directions, thus efficiently lubricating the cylinders, pistons, and camshaft before returning to the sump.

Two automatic valves control the oil pressure. One adjustable valve is mounted inside the engine in connection with the distribution gears, and the oil which escapes from it co-operates to lubricate the said gears. The other valve, which is not adjustable, is mounted externally on the crankcase and prevents damage to the air pressure gauge by preventing the oil pressure in the tubes from being raised higher than 64 lbs. to the square inch when starting up the engine from cold. The oil filler is situated on the left side of the engine base chamber, and it is best to warm the oil slightly before pouring it in. On the right side of the engine is the dip stick, a graduated rod which serves as an indicator to the sump oil level. This should be examined by drivers every 200 miles, and care should be taken that the oil in the sump should reach the graduation No. 5 and in no case exceed the mark No. 6. Excessive oil in the sump will cause

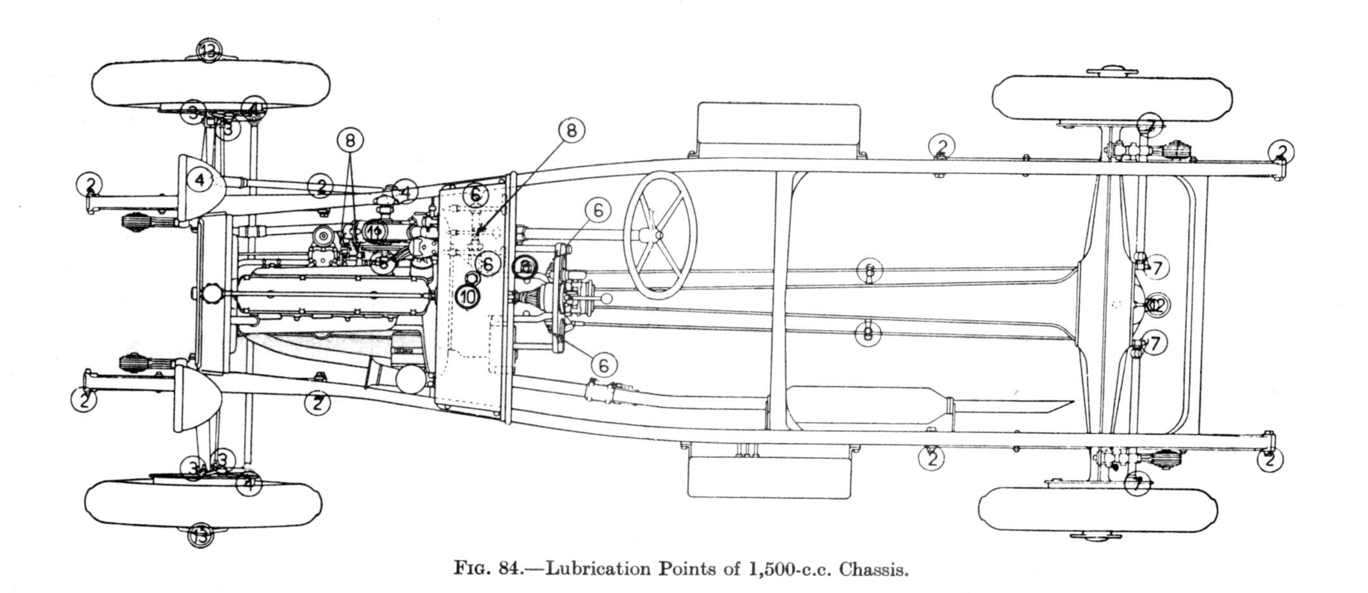

FIG. 84.—Lubrication Points of 1,500-c.c. Chassis.

the connecting rods to be immersed in the oil and thus originate trouble by intensifying carbon deposits on plugs, cylinders, etc.

Alfa-Romeo engines should have the oil completely drained out of the sump and clean oil replaced after every 1,500 miles or so. This should be done whilst the engine is warm. In lands where it is very dusty or sandy and a lot of grit may be taken in by the air intake of the carburettors, this draining of the sump should be done even oftener in the summer time.

On the super-sports model two gear pumps are placed in the sump; the oil, of which a considerable quantity is contained in a separate tank under the dashboard, is sucked up by the lower pump and sent to the crankshaft bearings, whence it is splashed in all directions as before, and then the oil is returned to the sump and is sucked by the upper pump and sent back to the tank.

Oil must never be fed directly to the engine, but exclusively to the tank under the dash on these models. Further, this tank should never be filled to the brim. Although it has a capacity of about 4 gals., not more than 3 gals. should be put into it, and it should never be allowed to be filled to more than 1 in. below the extreme upper edge of the inspection glass provided to show the quantity of oil in the tank. Care should be taken to verify the oil level only when the engine is warm, as that is when the oil has the greatest volume.

The ball bearing on the clutch shaft H, Fig. 75, p. 108, should be lubricated every 300 miles by means of a brush soaked in yellow grease. A travel of about $\frac{5}{8}$ in. of the clutch pedal, measured between the pedal plate and the footboard, is necessary before disengagement of this ball bearing is effected. This free play is indispensable for maintaining the clutch in good condition. Should it become diminished after long use, owing to wear on the discs, this should be remedied by reaching through the inspection port I and loosening the stop screws of the lever R to disengage it from the tube L of the pedal. The pedal should then be forced in such a way that the small levers G press against the bearing H.

This pressure should be kept up until the pedal itself has been brought forward for about $\frac{5}{8}$ in., after which the screw of the small lever R should again be tightened, thus completing the adjustment.

Should the coupling prove inefficient owing to wear on the discs, the three spiral clutch springs may be adjusted by screwing the three bolts N through inspection port I by giving an equal number of turns to each, though generally one or two turns are sufficient for such adjustment. When this operation is finished always remember to reconnect the three bolts to each other with the respective wires.

A compensating action is provided in the four-wheel braking system on these Alfa-Romeo cars, so that the power exerted on the brake pedal is distributed between the front and rear brakes by a compensator and subsequently by two geared compensators, through which the braking power is transmitted to the four brake rods. To adjust the brakes, first see that the ends of the levers at the ends of the small shafts of the rear brakes have a free travel of $\frac{3}{8}$ to $\frac{5}{8}$ in. before the wheels are locked when the pedal is depressed. Should this not be the case, the play of the levers is to be reduced to these limits by means of the adjustment turn-screws at each end of these two rods placed amidships in the chassis. Similarly, the front wheel brakes can be adjusted by screwing up the rod between the front wheel brakes and the side member of the frame. There is also a central adjustment which can give the proper tension to the brakes by turning it one or two turns and which is positioned under the floor boards beneath the driver. The compensator or turn-buckle should always be kept perpendicular to its respective rods, so if after a certain length of time an appreciable lengthening of the front brake rods is noted, they must again be brought to the proper tension by giving one or two turns to their adjustment in the forks ; and to keep the compensator perpendicular to its respective brake rod it will be necessary to also screw the interlocking rod in the same measure into its forks also. This last operation always alters the adjustment of the rear brakes, which must subsequently be readjusted after the previous adjustment of the front ones.

In regard to the brake on the transmission, adjustment is very simple and is accomplished by simply screwing up the fly-nut which is in the vertical return rod. The adjustment is correct when the hand lever travels one-fourth of its course before commencing to put on the brake. When cleaning and lubricating the brake rods, joints, etc., after dismounting the hub, toggle spindles, and brake drums, they should be cleaned with paraffin, and the opening cams and springs of the shoes should be lightly greased. Should the brake drum linings wear down to less than $\frac{1}{8}$ in., they should be renewed. If the steering requires adjustment, play in the ball joints can be eliminated by screwing up the plug which is parallel to the dumb irons and at the end of the rod. That plug, by means of an intermediate spring, presses on the bearings of each ball spindle. If there is longitudinal play in the steering, this is rectified by screwing up the plug provided on the steering column, while the side play of the gearing is regulated by the register.

Noticeable play between the teeth of the wheel and the thread of the screw can be taken up by turning the eccentric bearing of the small wheel shaft. This can only be done when the steering gear has been dismounted, otherwise it is necessary to give the wheel a turn of 180° in respect of the lever, after having first dismounted the latter, so as to place that part of the wheel where the teeth are still new in contact with the screw.

Should the Hartford shock absorbers become noisy, the central nut should be loosened and a little melted tallow poured between the friction discs.

ALVIS

FOUR-CYLINDER 12 H.P.

This car is a favourite with sporting motorists, as it has a high efficiency engine, overhead valve gear, and a cubic capacity of 1,645 c.c., which gives it a rating of 11·8 H.P. for what is known as the T.G. Alvis model, and 1,496·2 c.c. and an R.A.C. rating of 11·25 H.P. for the T.H. engine, which has been reduced in its bore and stroke in order to bring it in the 1,500-c.c. or 1½-litre class. Beyond that there are but few differences, these being the length in the crank throw, the modification in the pistons, and increased compression in the case of the T.H. model. The T.G. model is the standard touring chassis and the T.H. the sports chassis, and both are known as the 12-50 H.P. models.

The observer will notice that the engine base chamber is extended so as to obviate the use of an undershield under the engine; the cooling is by thermosiphon, and the radiator and cylinders hold 3¼ gals. of water. The removal of top and side covers discloses the valve push-rods, which are operated by a camshaft located in the base chamber of the engine. To dismantle the engine the first operation will be the removal of the top aluminium cover. Each valve is operated by a separate push-rod, which in turn is operated by a tappet, spring-loaded to prevent what is known as bounce. The upper extremities of the push-rods are fitted with a cup seat, and into these are fitted ball-ended adjusting studs. The upper end of the stud is slotted, so that it can be turned by means of a screw-driver, and nuts are fitted for locking the adjustment tightly into position. The correct clearance between the valve and rocker arm is, for both the exhaust and the inlet valves, ·003 in. As already stated in previous instructions, under no circumstances attempt to adjust the valve clearance when the engine is cold.

It should be possible to test whether the valve is seated properly by twirling the valve push-rods between the thumb and first finger, bearing in mind, of course, that if a valve is being opened, this particular valve and push-rod will not twirl easily.

The oil feed to the valve rocker shaft is controlled by a

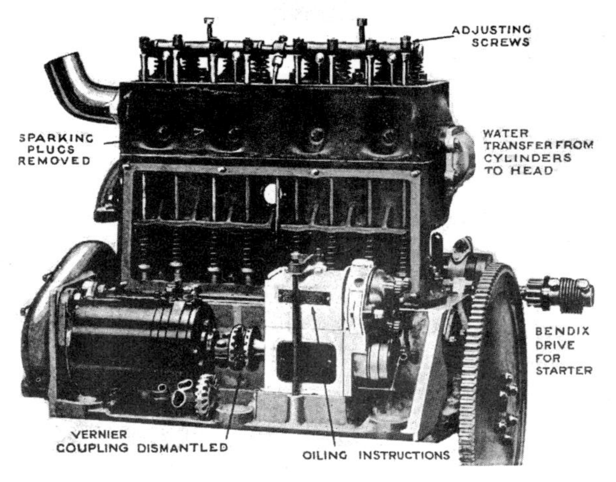

Fig. 85.

This shows the near side of the Alvis engine with top and side valve covers removed. The cap at the rear end of the engine between the cylinder head and cylinder block is the water passage way behind these two units. The self-starter and fly-wheel with relieved gear teeth are self-explanatory. The method of bolting the fly-wheel on the flange of the crankshaft is visible. In order to more clearly show the Vernier coupling between the dynamo and magneto, the rubber centre piece has been removed. The dynamo is attached by three bolts, the bottom one being a pivot bolt. The magneto can be removed in a few minutes; it has its own oiling instructions on the side. The bottom half of the base chamber has been removed and is not shown.

small metering screw in the centre of the rocker shaft. The adjustment is effected by this taper-ended bolt, and it will be found that by slacking off the locking nut, screwing the adjusting screw right home on to its seating and then undoing it two turns, the correct oil flow will be given. If, however, oil exudes too fast, close down the screw; but it must be remembered that it is unwise to race the engine with the top cover removed, or until the oiling circulation has had an opportunity of becoming warm. The oil should slightly exude from all centres of the valve rocker arms.

The valves are fitted into the detachable head and, so to speak, from underneath. It follows, therefore, that to remove a valve it is necessary to remove the detachable head, which is the ordinary standard practice with overhead valve engines; but it may be necessary at some time to change a valve spring, which can be done without removing the head.

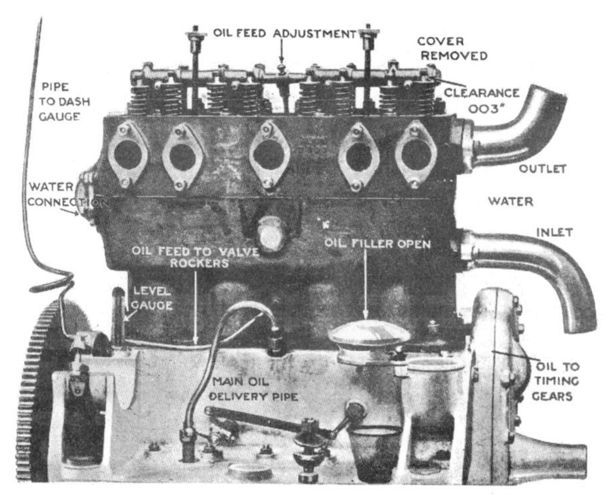

Fig. 86.

Offside of the Alvis overhead-valved engine, with top valve cover removed, disclosing valve operating mechanism, oil adjusting screw, and outside oil pipes. On the left of the base, the self-starter has been removed to clearly show the oil level rod, and on the right the oil filler cover swung round for filling and the gauze strainer removed. One of the engine holding-down bolts, with conical rubber seating, is seen in the foreground. These buffers, besides absorbing vibration, afford a resilient medium between the engine unit and the frame.

It will be seen that there are two springs to each valve, an inner and an outer spring. As the Alvis engine is capable of running at a very high number of revolutions, a positive type of valve-locking device is necessary, and that employed on this engine takes the form of a cup and two conical split keys, which register under the shoulder of the stem of a valve (see illustration). In Fig. 87 is shown the use of a simple home-made tool for compressing the valve springs; but it requires the assistance of a second person to extract and replace the valve collar. It will be noticed that two manifolds have been purposely cast in a single unit to form a hot-spot so as to preheat the gases before they enter the cylinders. Also note that the water circulation from the main cylinder block to the detachable head is effected by a by-pass at the rear of the cylinders, thus obviating the necessity of passage ways for the water through the copper asbestos washer which serves to make a proper gas-tight joint

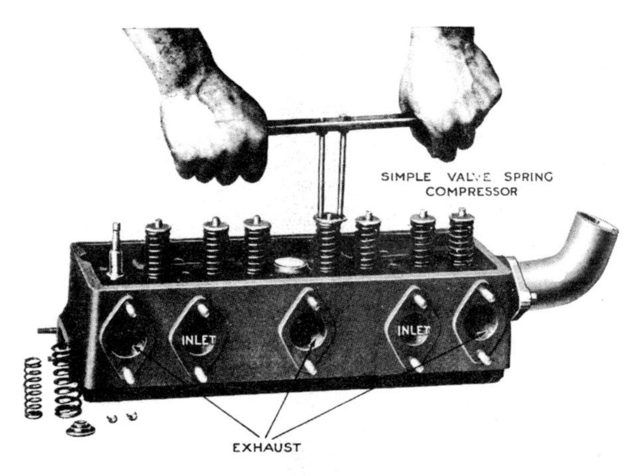

Fig. 87.

Cylinder head with valve operating gear removed, showing an operator using a simple tool to press down the valve spring cup to free the split collars. Another tool can be used when the rockers are in position, employing the rocker shaft as a fulcrum. The shape of the end of the stem of the valve on the left should be noted.

between the head and the cylinders. This by-pass is seen at the rear of the engine, and is formed by an aluminium cover plate and a canvas ply rubber washer. Also, it should be mentioned here that the correct firing order is 1, 2, 4, 3.

In taking off the manifold, it is as well to disconnect the carburettor first, after which all the nuts must be slackened off slightly, except, of course, those which will come off completely. Do not attempt to force the nuts loose, but note which one is holding most, and gradually withdraw the manifolds away from the cylinders while unscrewing. Dismantlement of the cylinder head is done by slacking off the ten $\frac{5}{16}$-in. nuts by which it is held down. The oil connection that feeds the valve rocker gear should then be disconnected, after which remove the aluminium water cover plate at the back of the cylinders. Mark the leads from the magneto when taking out the sparking plugs. It does not matter whether the tappet rods are removed before the cylinder head is lifted, or afterwards. The head can now be lifted, the top water outlet pipe being a useful lever. The cylinder head, which is made of cast iron, is fairly heavy. Fig. 88 shows the combustion chamber after the head is lifted, when

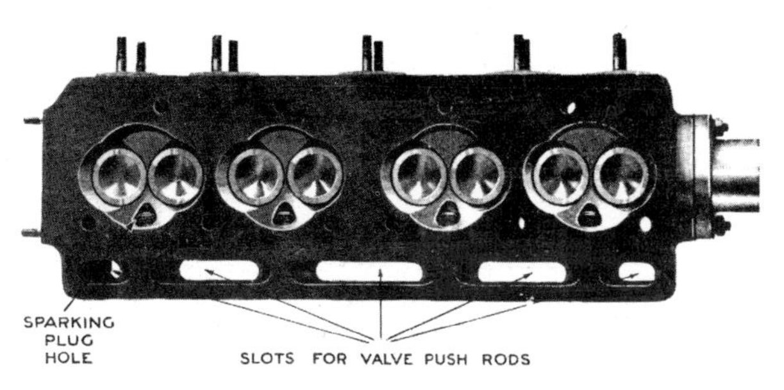

FIG. 88.

This is the detachable head of the cylinder turned upside down, showing the tulip-shaped valves in the spherical combustion chamber. Beneath the valves can be seen the screwed sparking plug holes. Ten holes are provided for the studs which pass through the head for the holding-down nuts. The slots on the lower side are for the push-rods which operate the valves, and not water passage ways, for which they might be mistaken.

the tulip-shaped valves are visible, as also are the ten holes through which the holding-down studs pass. On the lower side of the illustration the slots seen are the coring through the cylinder head through which the tappet rods operate.

For grinding in the valves, the operation has to be carried out in a slightly different manner from that to which most mechanics are accustomed, as it is not possible with that type of valve to fit a slot for valve grinding. If the rocker gear has not been taken off, it is possible to use this as a fulcrum to press down the valve spring cups, in order to extract the collars; but as there are two valve springs per valve, it requires a considerable amount of effort to compress them.

A simple method of extracting the collar is to put a little grease on the tip of the finger and, while the spring is compressed, to place the finger on the valve collars and they will usually stick to the grease and come away, leaving the valve cup and springs free. The illustration (Fig. 88) shows that the sparking plug hole is just below the valve, consequently a piece of bar $\frac{3}{8}$ in. diameter can be inserted through the sparking plug hole to hold the valve and prevent it turning, although in point of fact it cannot fall inside the cylinder,

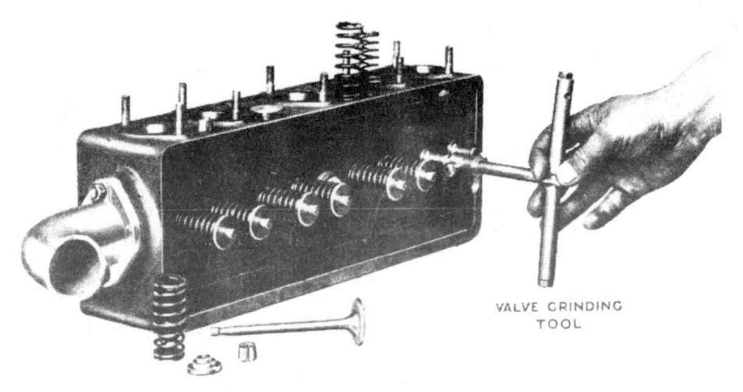

Fig. 89.

Owing to the tulip shape of the head of the valve, no cross slots are available for valve grinding. This operation is sooner or later necessary. The simple tool shown here can easily be made from an old tube spanner drilled and tapped to take two small bolts which grip the valve stem.

care being exercised to see that the piston meanwhile is not at the top. However, if the cylinder head has been removed, a block of wood should be inserted under the cylinder head, so that when the valve springs are compressed, the valve itself is prevented from being pushed out. The tool employed in valve grinding consists of a hollow rod tapped on either side to receive two set-screws and a cross-head which the operator holds in his hand, as shown in illustration (Fig. 89). With the aid of this tool it is possible to get a quick twirl or a semi-rotary motion for grinding; and the operator can push the valve off its seat at the same time.

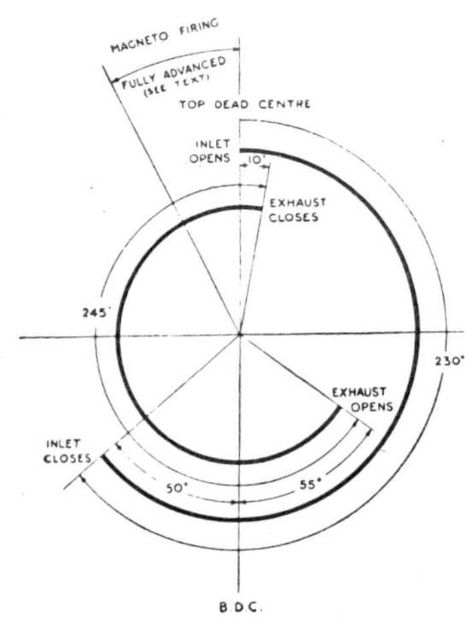

Fig. 90.—Valve Timing Diagram.

In timing the valves, as all are operated off the same camshaft, it is necessary to see that the inlet valve should open on top dead centre on the suction stroke, and it will follow that the opening and closing of the other valves will then be correct, provided that the tappet clearances are correctly adjusted. Following the firing order, the order of valve operation is 1, 2, 4, 3. The diagram (Fig. 90) depicts the

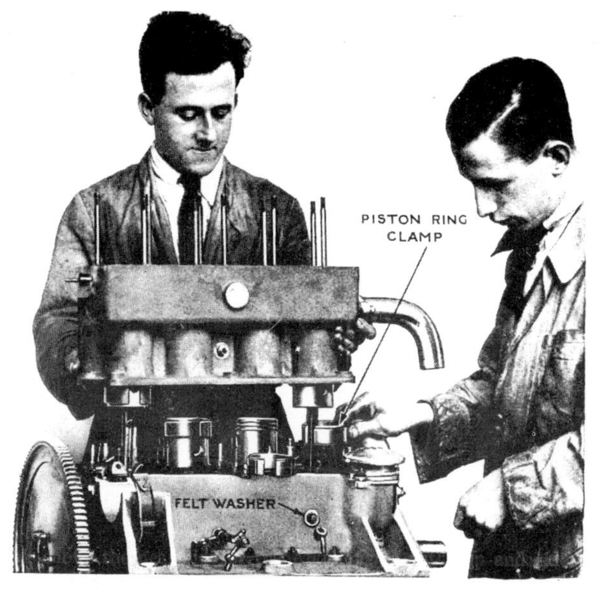

FIG. 91.

The removal of a cylinder block, showing that it is easier to take off the head first and then the block. The operator on the right is using a factory fitting, known as a piston clamp, which facilitates replacing the cylinder block, as by this means he does not have to compress the piston rings. With these clamps cylinder removal and replacement can be done by one person only, using a block of wood on which to rest the cylinder half way. The magneto control rod has been taken off the cross-shaft which passes through the base to show the felt washers which prevent oil leaks.

number of degrees measured on the fly-wheel: 1° measured along the circumference of the fly-wheel = 2·7 mm., consequently 10° measures a little over 1 in., or $1\frac{1}{16}$ in. exactly.

The cylinder block proper is secured to the base chamber by means of six $\frac{1}{2}$-in. nuts, and is easier to lift, as it is lighter than the detachable head. It should be lifted squarely, and while one person can do it alone, care should be exercised to prevent the piston from fouling the base chamber, because there is a tendency for the cylinders to draw the pistons upwards just before separating. The illustration (Fig. 91), by the way, shows the sort of clamps that are often used in replacing cylinders to permit the piston rings to enter easily.

The pistons are of aluminium alloy casting, each fitted with three piston rings, and below the bottom ring there is a circumferential groove cut, and holes are drilled at intervals to conduct excess oil back into the insides of the pistons,

Fig. 92.

General details of piston and upper end of the connecting rod assembly. The aluminium alloy piston is seen in the right foreground, having three rings and relieved below the lower one to return excess oil through the holes back to the sump. The gudgeon pin is held in the upper end of the connecting rod by means of a bolt seen to the left of No. 4 cylinder. No. 3 shows a tommy bar inserted to register the slot in the pin, and No. 2 shows how by means of a tube and a flat open-ended spanner the bolt is tightened. Remember to remove and replace the split pin which locks the nut tight.

and so prevent it entering the combustion chamber. A split pin locks the nut of the gudgeon pin bolt and prevents it unscrewing; this is a point of particular importance. To remove a piston, either two box spanners or a set spanner and box spanner are used, as the piston is drilled to permit the entry of the box spanner. The tommy bar of the box spanner can be used to correctly register the gudgeon pin in the connecting rod.

Unless the lower half of the base chamber is being removed when disconnecting a piston, it is as well to cover the holes in the base chamber through which the connecting rod passes with some rag, to prevent the inadvertent dropping of the nut or split pin inside the engine.

In order to more fully illustrate the manner in which the small end of the connecting rod is split and how the bolts pass through and clamp the gudgeon pins, these are shown removed in the illustration (Fig. 93).

The piston clearances between the piston and cylinder at

Fig. 93.

The first point of interest is the connecting rod, because this view could not be shown in Fig. 92. It can be seen how the rod is slightly split to allow the bolt to contract the rod on to the gudgeon pin. Next of interest are the helical cut timing gears. The lowest is the crankshaft, the large one on the camshaft phosphor bronze, and the right-hand drives the dynamo and magneto.

various points are as follows: top, ·915 in.; first ring, ·010 in.; skirt, ·004 in.; and it is considered by the manufacturers that these are the proper clearances to allow for the working expansion of the piston.

The timing gears consist of three helical cut gears, all of which are keyed on to the shafts, and the wheel centres are parallel and a tight fit on the shaft. Fig. 93 clearly depicts them, showing the front cover has been removed, and that the extension of this cover forms the starting handle bearing. To remove the gears it is necessary to use drawers, and the two steel gears are tapped for $\frac{3}{8}$ in. B.S.F. thread and a bronze gear $\frac{1}{4}$ in. B.S.F. thread. To make a drawer, use a piece of flat steel, drilling holes for the bolts which screw into the gears, and using a larger and coarser threaded bolt to act as the extractor. Retiming is facilitated by marking the gears. They are stamped with two 00 marks on the camshaft gear teeth and one 0 on the crankshaft. The magneto

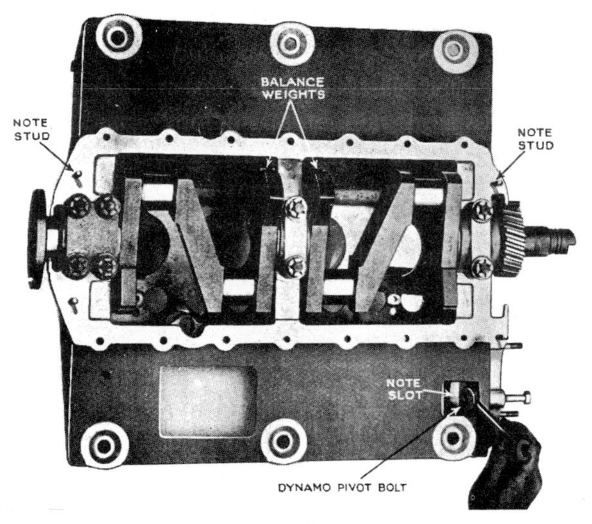

Fig. 94.

Lower half of base chamber removed. It is held in position by fourteen bolts and nuts and four studs and nuts, and there are two studs at either end. Note balance-weighted crankshaft and method of supporting it. The starting dog on end of crankshaft is part of the special nut holding on the gear. The seatings for the conical rubber washers are clearly visible, and the operator is indicating how access is obtained to the pivot bolt of the dynamo mounting through a hole in the extension of the base.

drive gear can be put into any position, because there is an independent timing for the magneto, which is coupled up to the dynamo shaft by a vernier coupling, consisting of two bronze ends and a hard rubber centre. On referring back to Fig. 85, p. 124, the coupling is shown dismantled.

The dynamo is mounted to the base chamber. When the engine is assembled originally the gears are correctly meshed and a line is scribed on the aluminium housing supporting the dynamo and the rear side of the timing cover. It will be noticed that the dynamo carrying plate is secured by three nuts, two studs, and one bolt, the one underneath the dynamo acting as a pivot, and the two holes in the cover plate are elongated or slotted to permit the dynamo to be rocked laterally. Unscrewing the two top nuts is quite simple, but in order to obtain access to the one underneath the dynamo, a slot is cut on the underneath side in the extension of the base chamber. Fig. 94 illustrates this.

Fig. 95.

This shows the top of the base chamber with cylinders and pistons removed, and, as well as can be photographically portrayed, the means of lubricating the camshaft. The centre bearing, the top bearing for the oil-pump shaft and rear camshaft bearing have a piece of the paper gasket or washer cut away sufficiently for oil to enter the countersunk holes. The oil pipe leading to the timing cover is not shown.

The same grade of oil is used for engine, gear-box, and back axle of the Alvis cars, consequently with the exception of grease used in the grease gun, Alvis owners can buy their lubricant in bulk and so save money. The standard oil is Castrol XL, but this must not be mixed with any other oil. As no drain plug or tap is provided for high level of the oil in the engine sump, it is very necessary to push the indicator downwards when refilling to see when it rises that it registers the exact contents in the engine and that the sump is not filled beyond the red mark on the indicator.

Drivers should remember that 1 quart of oil in the base chamber only is not sufficient to move the indicator, nor is it sufficient to cover the gauze strainer. Consequently with less than $\frac{1}{2}$ gal. it is not safe to run the engine. As a matter of interest, and in order to let an operator know the quantity of oil in the base chamber, 1 gal. of oil is equivalent to a level of oil 3 in. high in the base chamber, measured from the lowest point of the inside.

Fig. - 96.

This is similar to Fig. 59, with the crankshaft removed, but with camshaft in position, as well as oil-pump shaft driven by skew-gear off camshaft. The oil float and cross-tube on the left is for the magneto-advance control. The oil distribution tube has been marked, and this feeds the main bearings.

In reassembling the engine, the repairer must not forget the brown paper washer between the cylinders and the base chamber, as the joints between the cylinders and base chamber are made by painting the underneath side of the cylinder block and the top of base chamber with gold size, so that when these compress on the paper washer an oil-tight joint is made. When making the washer, the principal point to remember is to cut the paper away over the nut locating the centre cam bearing in position, and then to cut

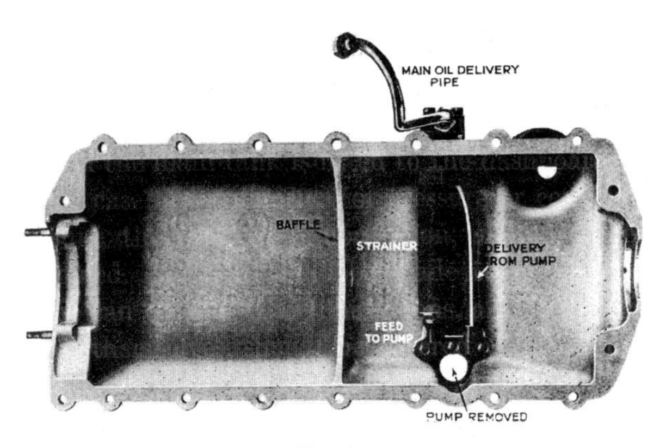

FIG. 97

In order to thoroughly understand the oiling system of the engine it is necessary to know how the lower half of the base chamber, or sump, is constructed internally. First, it is divided in the middle with a baffle-plate suitably drilled. A strainer is placed across the base conducting the oil to the pump, whence it is forced up to a block and thus from the inside to the relief valve situated on the outside of the base. The oil pump is not shown in position. Owing to the size of the gauze strainer, 1 quart of oil will not cover it. Remember this.

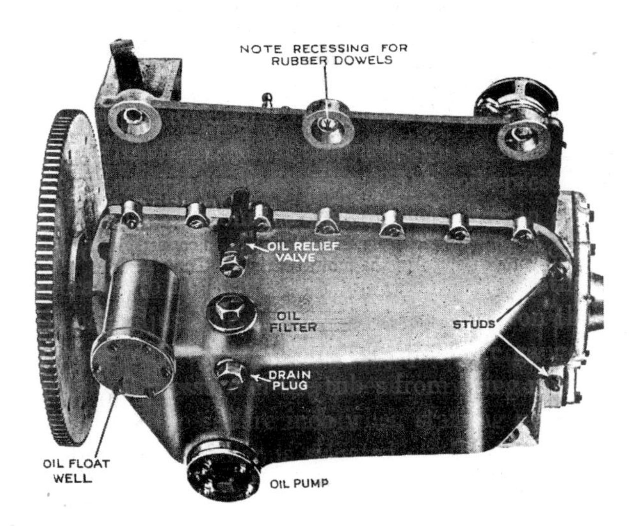

FIG. 98.

The lower half of the sump in position. This should be studied because the proper oiling of the engine has as much to do with the success in running as the manufacture itself. The pump is shown in position, then the drain plug; above this is the filter; above this again the relief valve housing and main oil conduit, and on the left, near the fly-wheel, the flat disc covering the oil level float.

the paper away sufficiently also between Nos. 3 and 4 inlet valve tappets so as to allow the oil to travel into the oil pump drive's spindle bush and finally to the back end of the rearmost valve tappet, to lubricate the rear camshaft bearing.

It will be seen in the illustration (Fig. 99) that the oil relief valve is depicted. It is bolted on to the outside of the base chamber, and contains on the underneath side a spring and a conical-seated brass valve with barrel extension and a hollow

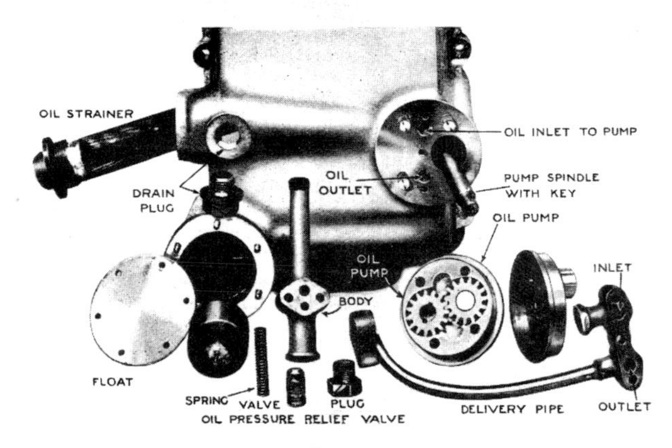

Fig. 99.

Working parts of the oiling system, showing strainer partly removed; also drain plug, oil level float, and, on the right of this, the oil-pressure relief valve in pieces, consisting of a tapered-seated plunger held in position by a spring and plug. Oil is delivered by the gear pump, driven by the shaft protruding through the base to the casting on the extreme right of the picture and so through the copper pipe to the main oil conduit and thence to the main bearings. The crankshaft is hollow drilled to feed the big ends.

centred brass plug. When the plug is screwed up into the body of the relief valve, it maintains the conical seating in place under the tension of the spring. As the engine speed increases, naturally the speed of the pump tends to increase the pressure in the oil circulation. Normal pressure should be about 25 to 30 lbs. when the engine is hot, and if the pressure overcomes the resistance of valve, some of the oil is then by-passed back into the base chamber. To increase the oil pressure if found necessary, a suitable shim or shims should be fitted under the spring and so increase its tension. The makers keep a supply of these shims if not obtainable elsewhere. If the oil gauge fails to register, or only registers a low pressure, after looking to see if the pressure is correct, remove the plug beneath the relief valve, take out the valve, clean it, and see that the spring is not broken.

Whenever an oil joint is broken, be sure to see that it is thoroughly clean before refitting, and when boiled oil is used or shellac, or some of the patented jointing compounds, be careful to see that it does not cover over the holes through which oil has to pass. When the cover plate over the valve tappets is removed, take particular care to see that this is put back evenly, and the fibre washers are between the plate and the nuts.

If at any time the repairer has to replace a big end bearing, care must be taken to clean out all oil ways and pipes before reassembling, especially the oil ways through the throws of the crankshaft, as these are usually overlooked. These are drilled $\frac{1}{4}$ in. diameter holes, so are not difficult to tackle.

A Solex carburettor is fitted with an ordinary setting of

Choke	24
Pilot jet	50
Main jet	110

The magneto supplied is a B.T.H. polar inductor type C.E. 4. The contact breaker is intended to operate with a gap of ·0012 in. when the contacts are fully open. The maximum advance on the T.G. standard model is 28° or $3\frac{1}{2}$ in. on the fly-wheel before top dead centre, and 34° or $4\frac{1}{4}$ in. in the case of the T.H. or sports model Alvis. The magneto spanner supplied with a guide forms the feeler gauge to this operation. A small mirror is useful in altering the gap without removing the magneto. There is one point in connection with the magneto which might puzzle a mechanic to find, and that is that a lead is taken from the engine side of the magneto on to the contact box cover. This is then held in position by a nut, and then the earth wire is attached separately. Sometimes the earth wire is removed in testing a magneto, but under no circumstances should the small wire above referred to be removed, or any attempt made to start the engine with the contact cover out of position, as the only result would be that it would not start until this has been replaced.

The electrical equipment is a 12-volt outfit, and when the battery is in good condition and properly charged, each cell should show from 2 to 2·2 volts.

The clutch is of the single disc dry plate type in which a centre steel disc is gripped between two friction linings by

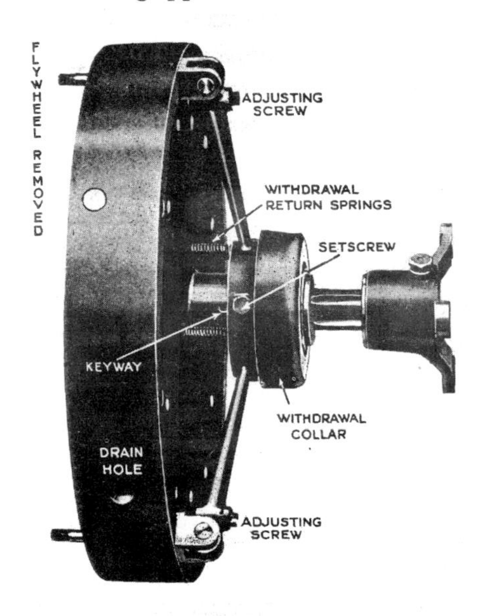

Fig. 100.

Clutch removed from fly-wheel, showing the general outward appearance. The coupling on the right hand is fitted with a greaser nipple, which can clearly be seen. The owner should take particular note of this point of lubrication, because, if neglected owing to being out of sight, the clutch will not work satisfactorily. It lubricates the clutch shaft attached to the floating plate. The manner in which the three ball ends of the levers fit into the withdrawal collar can be seen, as also can the return springs. The adjustment of the disengaging plungers by the set-screws is also clearly visible.

means of a number of springs. Fig. 100 shows it assembled, and dismantled from the fly-wheel in illustrations Figs. 101 and 102.

Should it be necessary to reline the clutch at any time, it is well to note that the dimension of the clutch lining for the outer diameter is $10\frac{1}{2}$ in. and for the inner diameter 8·4 in., that the thickness of the discs is $\frac{3}{16}$ in. and that there are thirteen aluminium countersunk rivets per disc, $\frac{3}{16} \times \frac{7}{8}$ in. long. To dismantle the clutch, the first operation is to disconnect the clutch pedal and slack off the bolt that clamps the clutch

Fig. 101.

The main components of the clutch dismantled, including the fly-wheel, floating clutch ring, clutch body, and central steel clutch plate and drive shaft. Through the hole in this shaft grease finds its way into the bearings in the clutch body. Note the grease slinger on the steel clutch plate and also how this plate is slotted, which overcomes the possibility of distortion and assists in dissipating heat.

Fig. 102.

Components of the clutch in the relative positions they occupy before the whole is bolted up into one unit. The friction disc on the clutch body cannot be shown in this illustration, but it can be clearly seen in Fig. 101. The keyways in the outer edge of the floating ring (friction-lined) are shown. These register in the keys in the clutch body. The three disengaging plungers can also be seen attached to the floating ring.

pedal levers on to the withdrawal shaft; then on knocking the levers outward from the centre, they will slip off the keys. The withdrawal forks will then swing backwards and permit the clutch to be lifted out after it has been unbolted. Some of the bolts which hold the body of the clutch to the fly-wheel pass through what are known as the guide keys for the clutch floating ring. There are three of these keys. Six ordinary bolts hold the clutch on the fly-wheel, and three with yoke

Fig. 103.

In order to show the means of testing engine and gear-box alignment by a simple tool, the fabric-jointed clutch shaft has been removed and lies in the undershield dissembled. The foot brake adjustment is visible in the picture. The outer ends of the clutch withdrawal shafts should be lubricated with grease gun, as these extremities are outside the undershield. The clutch stop is not shown in this illustration.

ends into which the clutch withdrawal levers are fitted. If it is necessary to dismantle the withdrawal collar with its ball bearing, this should be done as follows: The bearing is held in position by two spring steel rings, which rings can be dislodged from the groove in which they rest by prising the point of a scriber or similar sharp instrument beneath them, when the outer and inner portion of the withdrawal collar can be separated from the combined annular and thrust bearing.

A clutch stop is fitted on the latest models, which can be

set to operate at any point in the range of the pedal's travel, and is usually adjusted so as to bring it into action when the pedal is nearly fully pushed out, otherwise it is liable to come into operation when changing down.

If at any time it becomes necessary to realign the engine and gear-box, owing to the type of taper rubber buffers used,

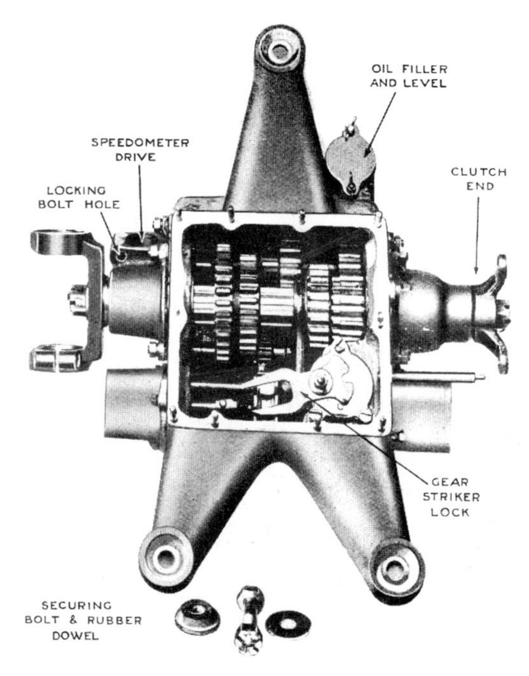

Fig. 104.

Gear-box with top cover plate removed, showing gear shafts and gears and selector mechanism. The fork-shaped lever slides to and fro with the gear lever, and it prevents more than one gear being engaged at any time. The front and rear box couplings are shown, as well as one of the rubber dowel buffers, by which the gear-box is mounted to the frame. The arms of the gear-box are recessed suitably.

either the engine or the gear-box can be aligned to the other. The illustration (Fig. 103) shows the clutch shaft has been dropped into the undershield and an aligning tool shown in actual use at the works attached to the front end of the gear-box coupling. It will be noticed that the underside members of the frame are particularly wide, and form at the same time both main and sub-frame.

The gear-box has four speeds and reverse, as seen in the illustration (Fig. 104). As each frame is jig-drilled in a special tool by the manufacturers of the car, the question of

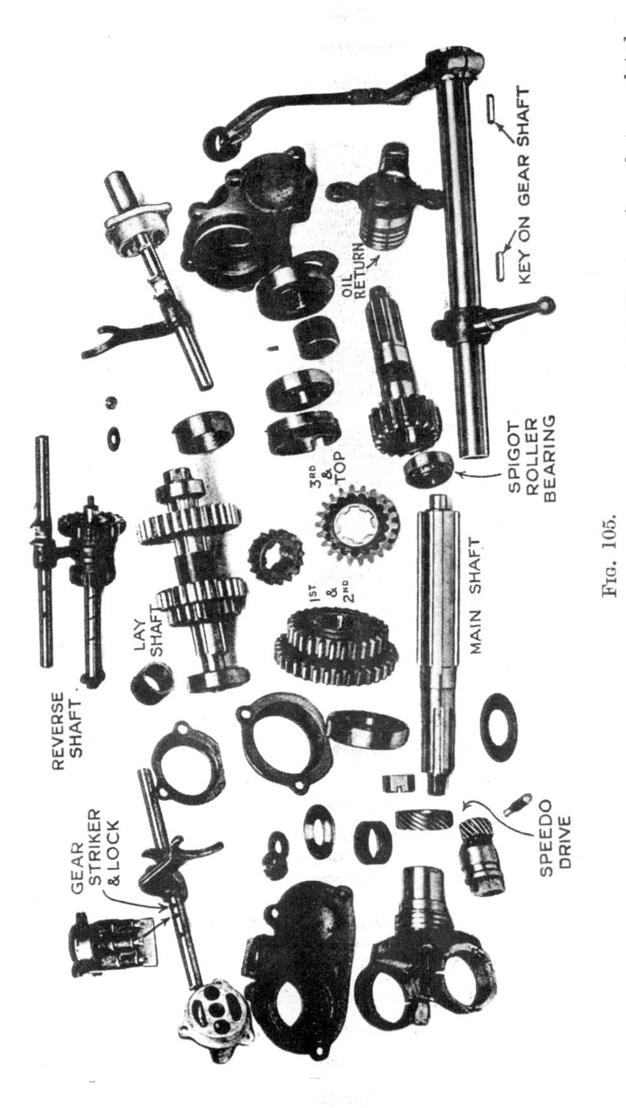

Fig. 105.

All the components of the gear-box shown dismantled. The parts are not just laid out anyhow, but co-related parts will be found near each other, as, for example, right across the front row will be found the various components of the main shaft, disregarding, of course, the gear lever assembly.

alignment needs very little attention on the part of a user as a rule ; but should adjustment be necessary, it will be found on tightening the nuts attaching both units, engine and gear-box, to the frame, that there should be a clearance of 2 mm. between the housing of the engine and sub-frame, and 3 mm. between the gear-box arm and sub-frame. It is easy to make a feeler gauge to measure this by bending a short length of $\frac{1}{8}$-in. flat iron at right angles to insert under the bearer arms.

In order to make the scriber used for alignment do its work properly, it is as well to chalk the clutch shaft coupling, and the scriber point will then show exactly whether the two units are in line or not.

Illustration Fig. 106 shows clearly how the universal joint

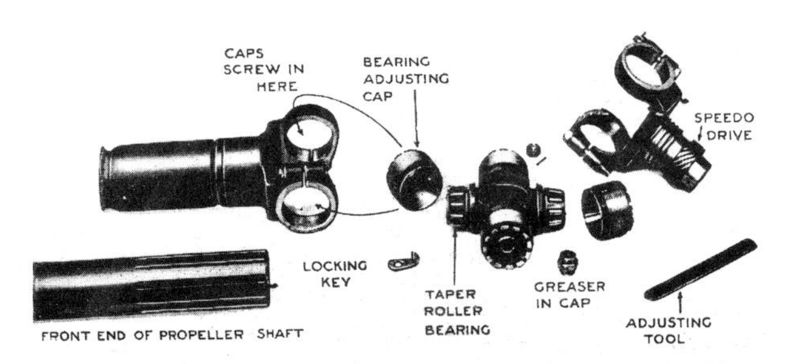

Fig. 106.

The front end of the propeller shaft with the universal joint dismantled. The rear end joint is similar, consisting of two crossheads and a star, to which are fitted taper roller bearings. It is grease-gun lubricated, and when dismantling this, be careful to replace the caps on the bearing to which they belong, and tie up the joint with string whilst dissembled.

is made. In order to adjust the crosshead of the propeller shaft, a flat tool should be made to tighten or loosen the bearing caps, and a piece of $\frac{1}{8}$-in. flat steel is suitable for this purpose. The bearing caps, as can be seen in the illustration, are threaded and are locked in position by a swinging key which registers in a groove in the cap. The cap itself is also held tight by the clamping bolt which tightens the split ends of the crosshead of the universal joint. Therefore, to dismantle or adjust, proceed as follows: To ensure that the rotation of the propeller shaft is not eccentric, a tool is made consisting of $\frac{3}{16} \times 1$ in. flat iron, which is shown in illustration Fig. 107, and has two $\frac{5}{16}$-in. pointed studs tapped in the end. A similar tool can be made for the front end and bolted to the side of the frame, only for the front end the bar will have to be twisted so as to make it come parallel with the propeller shaft.

Having clamped these two indicators in position, the bearing is roughly assembled, care being taken not to screw the bearing caps up too tight so that they prevent the shaft from turning freely. To carry out the adjustment, one cap must be slackened off and the cap immediately opposite tightened; then rotate the propeller shaft. This, of course, is done after one rear wheel has been jacked up, and it is necessary to see that the pointers indicate and the shaft runs true both from the side to side and up and down directions.

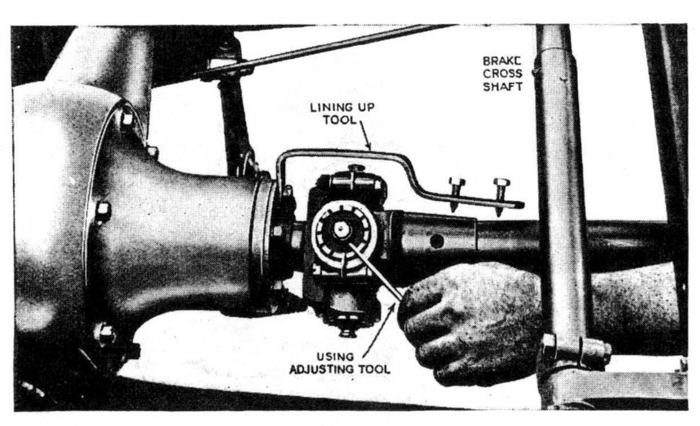

FIG. 107.

Rear end of propeller shaft and front end housing of rear axle. The operator is shown about to adjust the universal joint for proper alignment, only he has not removed the bolt and locking key. The flat metal bracket having two screws at the end is the tool used to check whether the shaft is running true. *Note.*—It is not part of the car, but part of the mechanic's tool equipment.

The illustration shows the operator with adjusting tool in use, but the keys which hold the cap in position will, of course, have to be first slacked off.

The whole of the interior of the Alvis rear axle can be removed for inspection with the aid of ordinary spanners and without removing the road wheels. This is done in carrying the whole of the differential crown wheel and driving bevel as a composite assembly on the front end extension housing of the rear axle. Removal of the rear axle shaft can be carried out by taking off the hub cap and screwing a $\frac{1}{4}$-in. B.S.F. bolt in the tapped end of the axle shaft, and the shaft can thus be completely withdrawn as it fits at its centre extremity into a castellated centre of the sun wheels of the differential. This $\frac{1}{4}$-in. bolt is provided in the tool kit, so can be used if the kit is available. The interior of the back axle can always be examined by taking off the rear end cover, because the rear end cover is only an inspection cover carrying the oil-filling extension, and there is no necessity to take off the front end cover unless dissembling the entire axle. Both front and rear end covers are machined in such a way as to correctly register in the aluminium casting of the main body of the axle. Consequently these parts should be assembled carefully

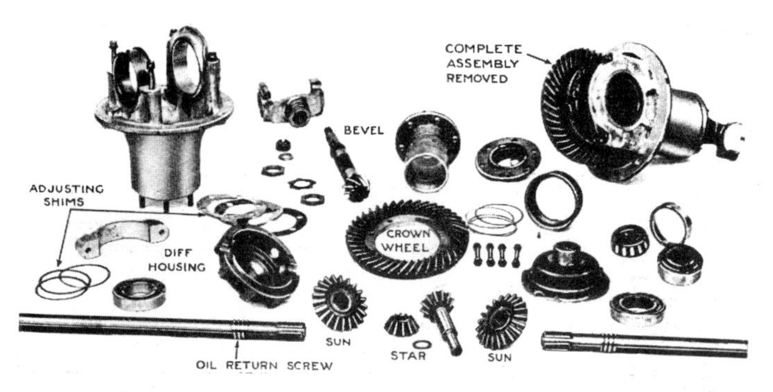

FIG. 108.—Rear Axle Interior Components Dismantled.

without force and with the aid of a rawhide mallet. Do not use a metal hammer.

The illustrations (Figs. 108 and 109) show the detailed construction of the rear axle. It is possible to remove the whole of the crown wheel and differential through the back cover plate of the axle, and no special instructions are needed, as it is a perfectly straightforward job. There is only one thing to be remembered by the repairer: that though the brake drums used for both rear and front axles are the same size, they are not interchangeable. Wheel extractors are unnecessary, as this is a full floating axle, and after the nut on the end of the axle tube has been removed, the entire hub and brake drum can be pulled off, disclosing the brake shoes. Care should be taken to see that the nut which holds the hub on to the axle tube extension should be properly locked in position by a countersunk screw and spring steel locking nut.

The front axle carries the brake drum and brake gear, consequently the rotating drum is bolted to the inner flange

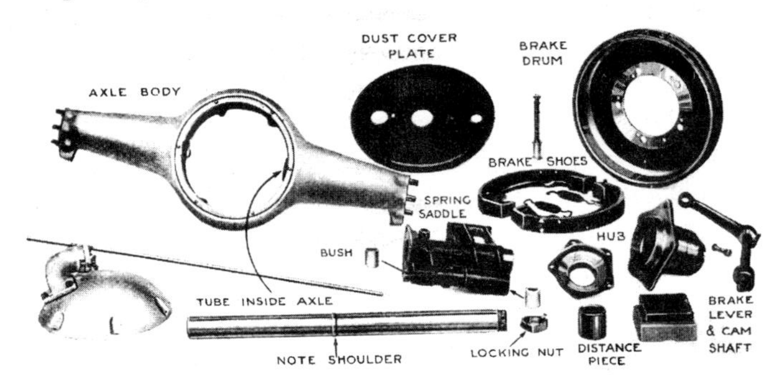

Fig. 109.

Axle casing dismantled with its various constituent parts. The steel tube is pressed into the aluminium body of the axle up to the shoulder. The load of the springs is taken on this tube, and, being extended, carries the ball bearings on which the road wheels run. Consequently the axle shafts do not take any load strains at all. See that the nut on the end of this axle tube is properly screwed up and locked whenever the wheels have been removed.

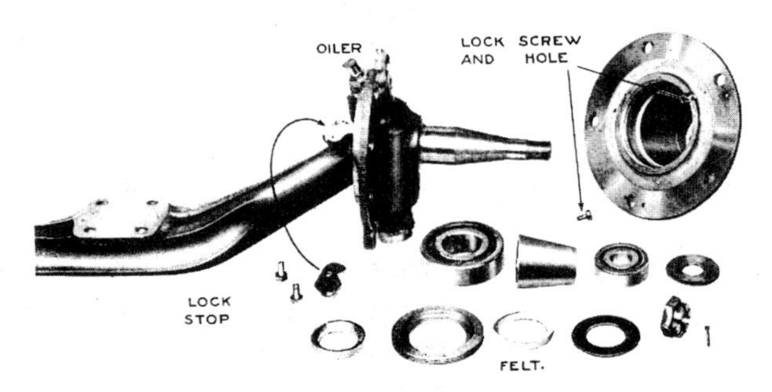

Fig. 110.

Front axle and steering head with axle parts dismantled. A point of interest is shown in the manner in which the grease-retaining washer-locking plate is secured; after being screwed up tightly a grub screw locks it in position. The plate carrying the brake shoes and brake levers, which is attached to the hub, has been omitted intentionally, as they are shown later in brake illustrations.

of the hub and the dust shield. Brake shoes are attached to the flange on a swivel head. The assembly of the hub on the stub axle is quite conventional, there being two ball bearings with a spacer between, and on the inside of the hub there is a felt grease-retaining washer locked in position by a screwed plate. This plate is also locked up by means of a cheese-headed grub screw. The amount of lock or swivel permitted to the stub axle is controlled by a stop, which is fixed on to the axle proper by two hexagon headed set-screws. One mentions this, though as a matter of fact this very seldom gets broken or wants replacing.

The steering head pin is forced into position under a pressure of about seven tons. Consequently it takes a considerable amount of force to remove it, and it is best removed by the use of a press. It can also be noted that it is of two

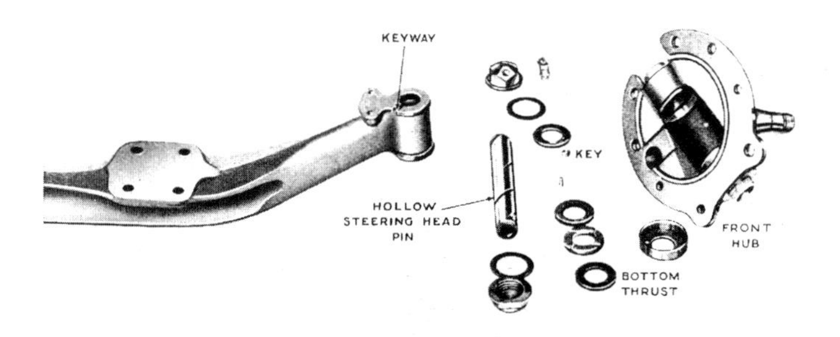

Fig. 111.

The steering head is simple, yet strong. Oil as lubricant is used, not grease. It should be noted that the steering head pin is pressed into the axle body under about seven tons pressure; consequently it will not be dislodged with a little tap. It is best to have it pressed out from below. Removal of the top and bottom caps allows the hollow pin to be cleaned right through.

different diameters, being $22\frac{1}{4}$ mm. above and 22 mm. below. The steering head is bushed above and below, and Fig. 111 shows the unit taken to pieces.

To dismantle the steering head, the only care needed is to note the sequence of the parts. These are given from above downwards. An oiler is screwed into a cap, which in turn screws on the top bush, and underneath this cap there is a flat washer turned up at one side to act as a lock. On the underneath of the top bush is fitted a hardened steel washer, which has a slot in it, and this slot must correspond with the groove in the top side of the axle head to allow a key to be inserted that prevents the hardened steel washer from rotating. Between the lower bush and the steering head of the body of the axle there is a thrust formed of two steel washers, with a thicker bronze washer between them ; but in order to

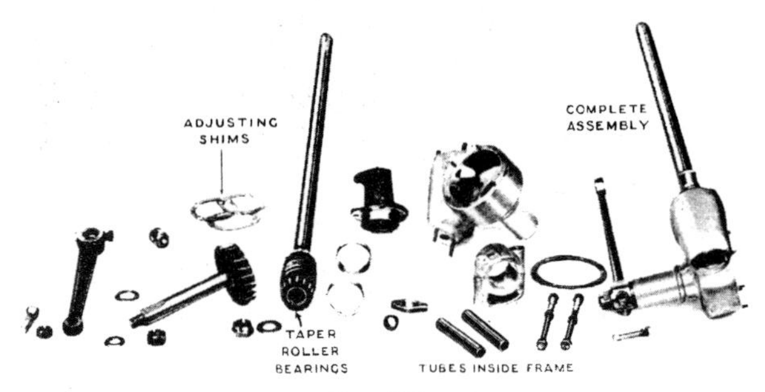

FIG. 112.

The steering gear is shown assembled on the right and also in its dismantled form. Adjustments are clearly given in the text. When one place on the worm wheel is worn, it can be turned round a quarter of a turn, and then there is a new wearing surface presented.

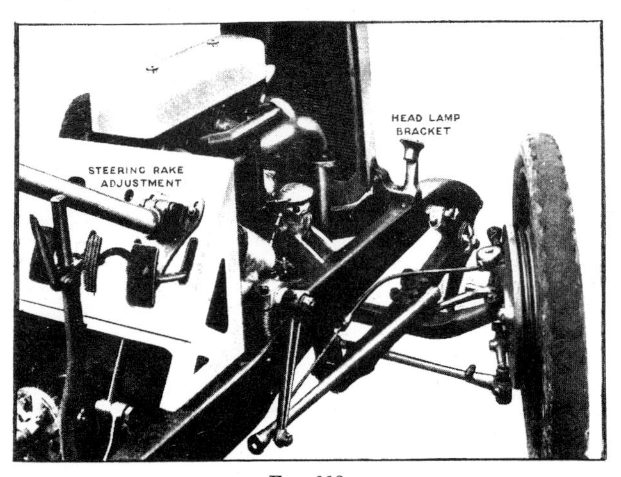

FIG. 113.

Off-side wheel locked round to show the lay-out of the steering, which is further assisted by dispensing with the scuttle and dashboard. The steering is well mounted on the frame and anchored on the aluminium footboard, the angle of rake being adjustable. There are no greasers on the pull and push rod. It has hard wood sockets. The tie-rod ends have greaser nipples. Note the combined head lamp and radiator support. Grease the cable where it enters the chassis support occasionally.

prevent the whole of the thrust race rotating as one unit, a small peg or dowel is forced into the body of the steering head, and this passes through the lower dust cover and the bottom steel washer, forming the thrust race. The idea of the dust covers is to exclude dirt and mud.

The underneath side of the lower bush is then fitted with a cap and washer, which is turned over to lock the cap in

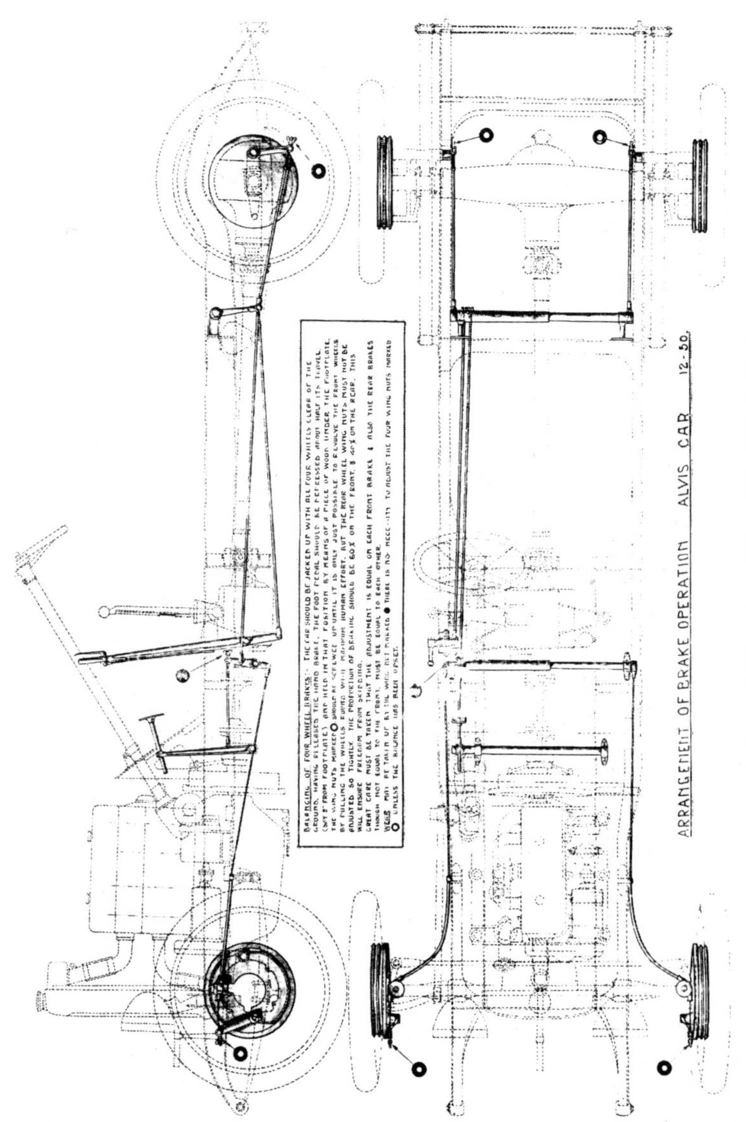

Fig. 114.—Plan and Elevation of Four-Wheel Brake System.

position. Lubricant, therefore, when inserted from above, will flow into the top bush and also through the hole through the steering head pin, and work its way upwards from the bottom cap into the bottom bush and thrust race.

The steering column is supported by a triangular plate and bracket on the aluminium floor boards, and the holes in the plate are slotted so that the rake of the steering can be altered. If altered, do not forget to alter the relative positions of the control rods, which are adjustable to compensate for any angle of the steering column. The nuts securing the

FIG. 115.

Rear end view of the chassis with body removed, showing the brake levers, rear brake adjusting thumb nuts and rear axle filler. Note that the brake operating shafts carrying the cams are lubricated by oil through large oilers. Be careful to cover up the oil holes by turning the cap round, otherwise water will enter instead of oil. The grease nipples on the universal joint can be seen.

steering column to the floor boards and chassis bracket should be periodically inspected and tightened if loose. This, of course, is more an owner's instruction than for a repairer, but it is a point which requires looking after. The fitting of the steering arm and the adjustment of the worm wheel and shaft are easy on the Alvis. The drop arm is attached to the worm wheel shaft, which has a squared end, by means of a bolt, which clamps the steering drop arm solid on to the shaft. The bolt in the top of the steering arm passes through a slot in the worm wheel shaft, consequently the large castellated nut which can be seen on the end of the worm wheel shaft, while in fact preventing the drop arm from coming off, is intended to maintain the worm wheel up against the bush on the inside of the box, and thus prevent side movement.

To adjust for wear it is necessary to slacken the bolt

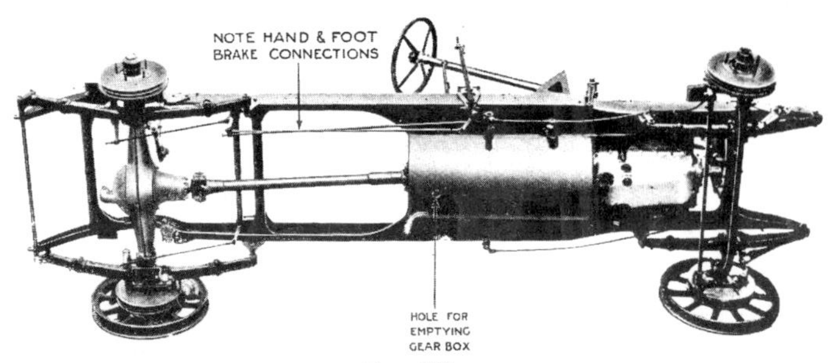

FIG. 116.

View of chassis, as seen below, in which the brake rods and levers can be clearly seen. The undershield is drilled to allow a box spanner to pass through to empty the gear-box without removing the tray. Although the engine needs no tray, scrape off the mud which collects from time to time on the base chamber. The same remark applies to the ribs of the brake drums. In both cases improved cooling will result.

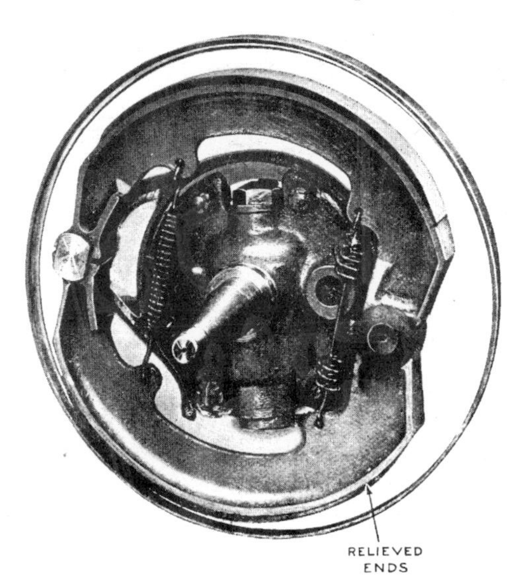

FIG. 117.

Front wheel hub removed from stub axle, showing brake shoes and pull-off springs. It is just possible to see how the brake linings are relieved at the outer ends. Do not overfill the front wheel bearing, otherwise grease will work out inside the brake drums and get on the shoes.

which secures the drop arm to the shaft before attempting to tighten the large castellated nut on the end of the shaft. Between the drop arm and the steering box there is a washer which fits on to the squared end of the shaft, where it protrudes through the box and thus will rotate with the shaft and arm. All the steering arms are fitted with detachable balls, and all the steering joints are adjustable for wear. It will be noted that the bottom of the main steering arm and the steering arm that is attached to the axle, which arms or levers are united by what are called the "pull and push

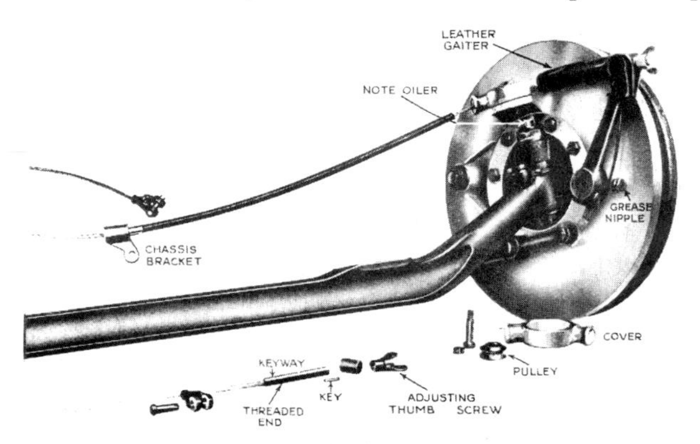

FIG. 118.

Front axle removed to show front wheel brake assembly. It looks simple, just a wire passing round a pulley and pulling a lever which operates a cam. Note greaser on camshaft and outside pull-off spring. Give the cable a little oil occasionally; it prevents rusting, although it is tinned. Beneath axle, the components of cable assembly are seen in pieces. In case oiler for steering head is missed, it is just below the small casting containing the pulley round which the cable runs, and requires a large quantity of oil to ensure the upper bearing being lubricated.

rods," are not fitted with greasers. The cups inside the pull and push rods are fitted with hard wood inserts, and on the end of the pull and push rods are fitted caps, locked into position by a turned-over washer. Taking up play of the steering joints, therefore, is a very simple matter.

Both ends of the tie-bar behind the axle are fitted with threaded couplings. By adjusting these it is possible to correctly track up the wheels at any time. The correct alignment with the car standing on level ground is that the front wheels should toe in $\frac{1}{8}$ in.

The adjustments of the brakes are effected by thumb nuts, five in all; the main one underneath the floor boards under the front seats takes up the general slack, and the other

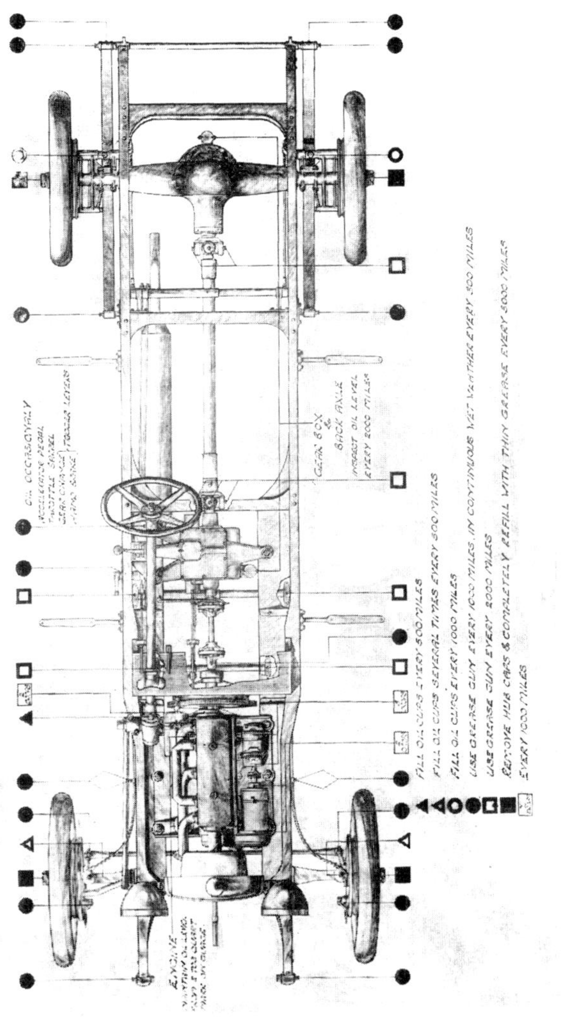

Fig. 119.—Oiling Diagram.

four thumb nuts on the actual levers near the wheels which operate the brakes are to be used for equalisation purposes. Illustration Fig. 116 shows the lay-out, and illustration Fig. 117 shows clearly how the dust cover which forms the

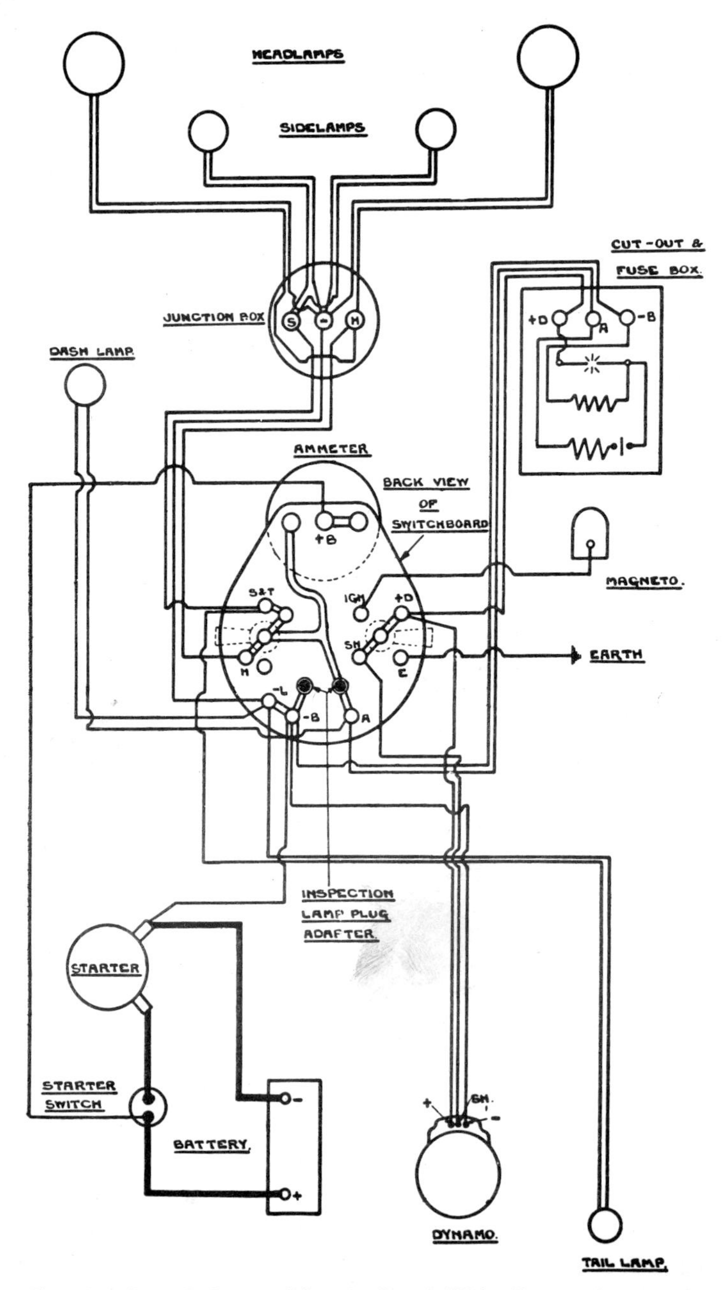

Fig. 120.—Lucas Lighting and Starting System Wiring Diagram for 12-volt Equipment as fitted to Alvis Cars.

anchor plate for the brake shoes is bolted to the swivelling stub axle, the front wheel having been removed for this purpose.

It will be noted that two different kinds of springs are used to contract the shoes on these front wheel brakes, which are opened in the usual way by a flat cam.

The cable employed to actuate the brakes from the foot pedal is $\frac{3}{16}$ in. in diameter ; and should new cable be required to be fitted, it is well to realise that the ends of the cable have to be splayed out into the countersunk recess of the front and rear end couplings, before these are soldered, to prevent them pulling through.

Fig. 121.

ALVIS SIX CYLINDER

The chassis details of the six-cylinder Alvis model are so similar to those of the four-cylinder that there is no need to recapitulate for this chassis what has been previously written for the smaller one. The engine has a bore and stroke of 63 × 100 mm., giving a cubic capacity of 1,870 c.c., and the model is commonly known as the TA. The electrical unit consists of a 12-volt 51 amp. battery, type TR9, Lucas type T5CF dynamo, and Bendix operated self-starter SD8. The six-cylinder timing diagram is given below, as that differs from the four-cylinder and is self-explanatory, the firing order being 1, 5, 3, 6, 2, 4.

While it is possible to put a cylinder block back single-handed, it is best effected by two operators, as already stated ;

but in the case of a four-cylinder engine the pistons are either at the top or bottom of the stroke, whereas with the six-cylinder engine the throws of the crank are set 120°. Therefore on replacing the cylinder block for the six-cylinder Alvis, it is best to start with the centre pair of pistons, and it will follow that Nos. 2 and 5 will next enter, and finally the front and rear pistons.

The carburettor fitted on the six-cylinder is the Solex MOV 30 mm., and the standard setting is :—

Choke, 26 ; pilot jet, 52·5 ; main jet, 125.

This setting is stated to give an average fuel consumption of about 30 miles to the gallon.

The magneto on the six-cylinder Alvis is the same type of BTH polar inductor as used on the four-cylinder. The contact breaker is intended to operate with a gap of ·012 when the contacts are fully open, similarly to the four-cylinder model, but the maximum advance on the TA six-cylinder Alvis is $43\frac{1}{2}°$ or $4\frac{5}{8}$ in. on the fly-wheel before T.D.C., this differing from the four cylinder.

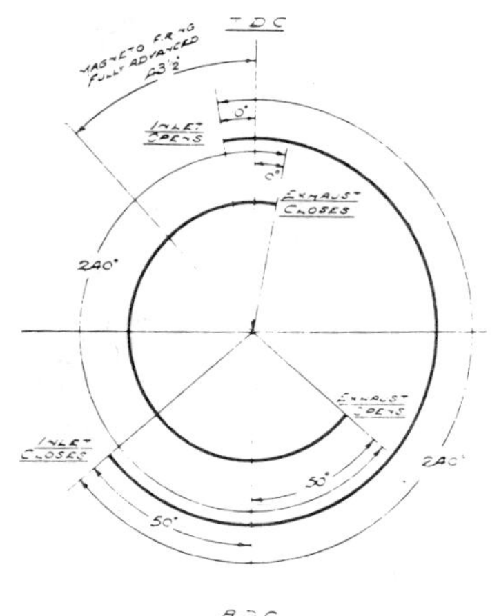

Fig. 122.—Six-Cylinder Timing Diagram.

The oiling chart and electrical equipment are practically the same, so are not repeated.

ALVIS FRONT WHEEL DRIVE

The most recent model of the Alvis range is that with the front wheel drive, in which a 1,500 c.c. Sports Alvis engine is fitted, driving forward through a gear-box and through bevel gear carried on the frame. The drive is transmitted to each front wheel by short cardan or driving shafts, with a universal joint at either end. Each wheel is independently sprung, otherwise the general lay-out is similar to the Alvis chassis already dealt with. The illustration shows the front view of this new Alvis car and the independent front wheel suspension.

FIG. 123.—Alvis Front Wheel Drive.

BENTLEY

FOUR AND SIX CYLINDER

THREE-LITRE BENTLEY

All Bentley chassis are covered by a five-year guarantee, so that the ordinary repairer seldom sees one of these chassis in his shops, except for very minor adjustments, as their owners usually send them back to the Bentley service station at Hendon. At the same time, proprietary articles such as are included in the electrical equipment, shock absorbers, magnetos, etc., are not included in the Bentley Motors Ltd. five years' guarantee, although they are in most instances covered by their manufacturers' one-year guarantee. At any rate, it is as well for the repairer to have this knowledge in his mind, so that when a customer comes to him he can ascertain by the date of the car whether the item is covered by one of these guarantees before proceeding to do the work.

The 3-litre Bentley is the oldest and most popular model, as it is only since 1927 that the larger six-cylinder Bentley and the four-cylinder 4½-litre Bentley have been put upon the market. Consequently, though a few points are given in these notes in reference to those two models, it is the 3-litre Bentley which is given in greater detail, as the second-hand cars have good reputations and so pass frequently from owner to owner after the guarantee has expired.

There are two models of the 3-litre Bentley: the standard model with a wheel base of 10 ft. 10 in. and the speed model with a shorter wheel base of 9 ft. 9½ in. Both have a track of 4 ft. 8 in., while the weight of the standard chassis is 24¼ cwt., and that of the speed chassis 22¾ cwt. The capacity of the engine sump is 2½ gals., that of the petrol tank being 11 gals. Both have detachable wire Rudge Whitworth wheels, and the standard tyre is a Dunlop 820 × 120 mm. Two M.L. magnetos are incorporated in the engine fitting; but while the standard model uses a Smith-Bentley five-jet carburettor, the speed model has a twin S.U. carburettor. The autovac system is common to both.

The engine has its four cylinders cast *en bloc* of 80 × 149

FIG. 437.—3-litre Bentley Short Chassis (1928), front view with wire guard fitted in front of radiator.

mm. for the bore and stroke respectively, which gives it a rating of 15·9 H.P. with a cylinder capacity of 2,996 c.c. Each cylinder has two exhaust and two inlet valves. These are tulip shaped and their diameter is small, which enables them to function for a very great mileage without attention, and consequently they seldom require grinding in. The cam-shaft is mounted centrally along the top of the cylinder block, and runs in five plain phosphor bronze bearings. There are two types of rocker gear which operate the valves. The earlier type consists of rockers which are mounted on two rods, which are located parallel with and on either side of the camshaft. The rockers have at one end a hardened steel pad, which takes the lift of the cam, and at the other end a tappet screw secured by a lock-nut. This screw bears on the end of the valve, and by means of it the tappet clearances are adjusted. The valve tip and tappet screw are also hardened to prevent wear. The later type rocker gear consists of duralumin

FIG. 438.—Bentley 3-litre Engine, Sports Type (1928), showing two carburettors, magneto, autovac, and general lay-out.

rockers having in one end a hardened steel roller which bears on the camshaft, and at the other end a ball-ended tappet which depresses the valve. The tappet screw is secured by a lock-nut. The ball ends are flattened at the point where they bear on the valves and are free to rotate in the ends of the tappet screws, thus always bearing on the full surface of the valve end. In the early Bentley 3-litre engines the valves were fitted with detachable hardened caps, in order that they could be renewed if required. This is a point that the repairer can look for when in doubt as to the year or age of the motor requiring attention. There are two springs to each valve.

The valve gear and actuating mechanism are entirely enclosed in an oil-tight cover. The crankshaft is carried in five white metal bearings, and is prevented from moving endways by a double thrust ball race, housed behind the starting handle bearing. This ball race also takes the thrust imposed by the withdrawal of the clutch. Aluminium pistons are

FIG. 439.—3-litre Bentley Engine (1928), near-side complete, showing cut-out on dash and stop for front spring (in front of silencer).

fitted, having four rings at the top. The camshaft drive is by means of spiral bevel gear and a vertical shaft from the front end of the crankshaft.

The engine oiling system is actuated by an oil pump situated at the bottom of the sump at the forward end. The pump is of the gear wheel type, and is driven by a spindle rotated by worm gearing off the forward end of the crankshaft. Means are provided for adjusting the oil pressure, which is controlled by a spring loaded ball valve.

The oil pressure should only be adjusted after the engine

has been running an hour on the road, and the oil is therefore thoroughly hot. The approximate pressure recommended is 12 lbs. per square inch, at a road speed of 30 miles per hour on top gear. To adjust the pressure on the earlier 3-litre engines, the adjusting plug will be found on the off-side front of the oil tank underneath the crank-case. The lock-nut securing the plug is slacked back and the plug screwed inwards (*i.e.*, clockwise) to increase the pressure and outwards to decrease the pressure. Should the pressure drop unduly for no apparent reason, it is probably caused by dirt underneath the pressure release valve, preventing the latter from seating properly. This can frequently be rectified by slacking back the lock-nut and giving the adjusting plug half a turn one way and then half a turn the other way. If, however, this is not effective, it will be necessary to completely unscrew and remove the plug, take out the spiral spring found underneath and remove the ball. To remove the ball a receptacle should be placed underneath the plug hole ; when the engine is started up the pressure of oil will force the ball out into the receptacle. Then wipe the valve seating with a non-fluffy rag and replace the parts, screwing down the plug before starting up the engine so that oil pressure will develop immediately.

On later engines the adjusting plus is mounted in the flange of the sump immediately forward of the oil filter on the near-side of the engine underneath the oil filler. The lock-nut securing the plug should be slacked back and the plug screwed downwards to increase and upwards to decrease the pressure. If loss of oil pressure makes it necessary to remove the ball, the adjusting plug must be removed by unscrewing the two screws securing the flange, the flange, plug, lock-nut, and spring coming away as a unit.

The ball can then be removed by means of the special tool provided in the tool kit. The split end of this tool is pressed down on top of the ball and is expanded over it, enabling its withdrawal. The seating can then be cleaned by wrapping a piece of non-fluffy rag round the end of the tool and rotating it backwards and forwards on the seating. The parts are then replaced.

It should also be realised that when the oil in the engine has not been changed for a big mileage, the oil loses its body,

FIG. 440.—3-litre Sports Bentley Engine (1928) showing two magnetos, water pump, fan belt, and drive, also portion of two S.U. carburettors.

which may account for the loss of oil pressure. This should therefore be taken into consideration before looking for other reasons for the lack of pressure.

Another possible cause of loss of oil pressure would be a dirty oil filter. This should be looked to before attempting other work; but a blocked-up filter is unlikely if the instructions with regard to cleaning it every 5,000 miles are carried out. At the same time, the oil filter is more likely to get choked on a new car than on one which has been on the road for some time.

The oil supply is replenished through a filler on the near-side of the engine, the oil passing through a large cylindrical gauze. Before reaching the bottom of the sump, the oil has to pass through another gauze, which is flat and of large area.

To ascertain the quantity of oil in the sump on early type engines, a dip stick is fitted in the crank-case under the oil filler. There are two marks on the dip stick—the higher shows when the tank is full, and the lower is the mark below which the oil level should not be allowed to fall. On later engines a gauge of the float and rod-type is fitted on the flange of the sump underneath and just forward of the oil filter. The gauge is contained in a cylindrical glass case, on which are two marks. When the top of the rod is level with the upper mark, the tank is full; when level with the lower mark, the oil is at the lowest point at which it should be allowed to go. The quantity of oil required to raise the level from the lower mark to the higher is approximately 1½ gals.

When replenishing the tank, plenty of time should be allowed for the oil to filter through the two gauzes before judging the level, and the colder the weather, the slower the oil—which is then thick—filters. With the car standing on level ground, the oil level should be tested before starting up in the morning, so as to make certain that all oil in circulation has had time to drain back to the sump. Care should be taken not to overfill, as this will cause excessive oil consumption.

The oil, on leaving the sump and before passing to the bearings, is forced through the cylindrical gauze filter. On early engines this is a separate unit mounted immediately behind the radiator on the near-side. On later engines the filter is contained in the flange of the sump on the near-side, immediately forward of the oil level gauge. The container of the filter is an integral part of the sump. On leaving the filter, the oil passes through the side of the crank chamber and is led by branching pipes to the five crankshaft bearings. Oil ways are drilled in the crankshaft, through which oil passes to the big end bearings. It is then thrown by centrifugal force into the crank chamber and so on to the cylinder walls, thus lubricating the pistons and gudgeon pins.

The camshaft has an oil passage throughout its length. Oil is fed into this through the rear end bearing, the supply being delivered through a pipe taken off the delivery side of the filter. Thus the five camshaft bearings, cams, rockers, and guides are lubricated. The overflow of oil from the overhead gear returns to the sump through the vertical shaft housing and two return pipes, situated between cylinders Nos. 1 and 2, and Nos. 3 and 4 (No. 1 cylinder being nearest to the radiator). Thence it drops to the sump through the large gauze filter mentioned above. All carbon and sediment is therefore trapped, and it will be noted that the oil is filtered before and after passing through the engine.

Two magnetos are fitted and two separate sets of sparking plugs, four being mounted on the exhaust side and four on the inlet side of the cylinder block. The magnetos are mounted on flanges on either side of the vertical shaft housing, and they are driven at either end of a short cross-shaft, which in turn is driven off the vertical shaft. The magnetos are two separate units and are synchronised to spark simultaneously, although they are controlled by separate switches. The order of firing of the cylinders is 1, 3, 4, 2. It is important that both of the switches should be on when the engine is running.

To synchronise the magnetos, set the off-side magneto fully advanced at 45° before top dead centre, this point being marked on the fly-wheel, then by rotating the other magneto on its flange, set it approximately correct by eye. Next turn the engine backwards and place in between the points of the make and break on each magneto a piece of cigarette or tissue paper. As soon as the off-side magneto reaches 45°, the points will open and release the paper. The other magneto should then be rotated on its flange until it releases the corresponding piece of paper at the same moment.

K.L.G. plugs, type J. 1, are fitted to the standard 3-litre engine, and type F. 12 to the speed model. After running, the points open out; it is therefore advisable to remove the

Fig. 441.—4½-litre Bentley (1928), showing front view of *full* wheel lock, front wheel brake arrangements, also lamp setting and Tecalemit lubrication points.

plugs every 3,000 miles and set the points to the gauge on magneto spanner, or ·019 in. To clean the plugs, remove the brass nut just above the main body of the plug; the whole of the inside of the plug then comes away and can be cleaned with a rag. The centre part or electrode of the plug can be replaced when worn out.

On the standard long chassis a fan is fitted, and the temperature of the water in the cylinder block is regulated automatically by a thermostat. The water is circulated by a vane pump, situated immediately behind the radiator and mounted on the front portion of the vertical shaft housing. It is driven off the magneto cross-shaft. The thermostat is situated on the near-side front of the cylinder block, and the action is such that when the engine is cold, the water circulation is short-circuited and does not pass through the radiator. The temperature, therefore, rises rapidly until it reaches approximately 75° C. or 167° F. A valve in the thermostat then opens and the radiator is brought into operation.

The speed model engine is not fitted either with a fan or a thermostat.

The dynamo is mounted on the rear face of the dashboard. It is driven from the rear end of the camshaft, the connection being a short coupling and two hardy fabric joints, which allow for any relative movement between the dashboard and the engine. The dynamo acts as a fly-wheel also on the camshaft, damping out torsional vibration and operating at half-engine speed. It is very easy to get at should occasion arise, but it should be noted that on the 1922 Bentley 3-litre chassis, the dynamo was geared up to run at three times camshaft speed.

The starter motor is housed in the crank-case casting on the near-side of the engine, and is held in position by a taper cotter pin. The motor is therefore easily removed, if for any reason this should become necessary. Should it be found that when the starter switch is depressed the starter revolves without the Bendix pinion engaging in the fly-wheel, it is advisable to remove the aluminium cover and wash the worm of the Bendix drive with petrol. It should never be oiled, as this collects dirt, which makes the Bendix mechanism sticky.

The clutch is of the inverted cone type, with the cone faced with Ferodo, and it drives through a ring secured to the fly-wheel by bolts. On the ring are tongues which cause the clutch to take up the drive smoothly, even though the clutch pedal may be suddenly released. When the clutch pedal is depressed, the clutch is disengaged by the pressure of two rollers on a thrust ball race. The mountings on which these rollers are carried are so compensated that the pressure exerted by them on the thrust race is always equal. The thrust of the clutch spring is taken by a thrust ball race at the front end of the spring inside the cone. Lubrication of

FIG. 442.—3-litre Bentley (1928), showing clutch, clutch stop, gear-box, brake-adjusting rods, and universal joints.

the spigot and thrust ball race is effected by a wick lubricator, which is screwed into the end of the crankshaft, and is fed by the same supply as the main crankshaft bearings.

If the clutch is inclined to be fierce, push out the clutch, and with the end of a thin blade insert a little graphite grease between the clutch ring and the cone. In order to ensure it getting over the whole face of the clutch, this should be done in three or four places. If the clutch sticks and is hard to disengage, try squirting some petrol on the face of the lining. All lubrication of the clutch spigot bearing is automatically done by the engine.

On 1922 3-litre Bentley cars, some of the clutches had noisy withdrawal races. If on withdrawing the clutch a loud squeak is heard, this is due to the clutch withdrawal races being in need of lubrication. Engine oil should be applied by means of an oil can, the rollers being lubricated both on the outside and inside.

FIG. 443.—Front View, Six-Cylinder Bentley (1928) Chassis, showing dynamo and front wheel brake lay-out.

The shaft connecting the clutch to the gear-box has a sliding splined joint at its front end, and in chassis later than 1923 a Hardy disc coupling at its rear end. The shaft is hollow, and an oil gun connection is provided through which it is loaded with oil, which lubricates the front coupling only.

Decarbonising the engine is a matter which the Bentley Company insist should be done either by themselves or by an authorised service agent, so long as the car is within the guarantee. The Company's permission in writing must be obtained if the work is to be done by anyone else, or the guarantee will be affected.

Certain parts of the engine and chassis are sealed, and these seals must not be broken except by the Company or their authorised service agents, except after the makers' guarantee has expired.

The procedure for decarbonising, however, is as follows (one mentions this for Bentley's outside the guarantee) :—Remove water connections to radiator and carburettor. Remove dynamo drive at rear end of camshaft, leads from sparking plugs, and the sparking plugs themselves. Remove clip on vertical housing just above the magneto cross-drive, and remove the petrol pipe, autovac, and horn. Then take the cylinder holding down nuts away and lift block.

To grind in the valves, remove cam-case top cover and bridge piece which holds down the rockers. Remove the camshaft and the valve springs, as well as the valve guides and the valves, as the valves cannot be removed before the guides have been taken out. To remove or change a valve spring, it is necessary to take away the cover over the valve and the bridge piece holding the rockers in position, as already mentioned; then remove the rocker rod, together with the rockers, taking great care when replacing to tighten the bridge piece down evenly, otherwise it may fracture. Remove the sparking plug in the cylinder in which it is desired to change the spring; but, of course, these will all be taken out when decarbonising, though it is advisable to remove the plug on the opposite side of the cylinder to which the valve in question is, so that a direct push can be maintained on the underside of the head of the valve. Now push down the valve spring collar, which is the round disc on the top of the spring; this will allow the two tapered cotters to be removed. Remove the collar and change the spring if necessary. When replacing the rockers, make sure all the tappets have clearance, and readjust as soon as possible when the engine is thoroughly hot.

To grind in valves it is necessary to make a special tool to hold them and grind from the top, as, owing to their shape and the cylinder head, they cannot be ground in with a screw-driver from below.

On no account remove the lower half of the cam-casing, which is integral with the upper half of the vertical shaft. When replacing the cylinder block, take care that the paper washer has all the necessary holes in it, the two most important ones being those centrally placed between Nos. 1 and 2 and between Nos. 3 and 4 cylinders. These holes are connected with the overhead gear, and drain the oil from there to the crank-case. When lifting and replacing the cylinder block, the greatest care should be taken that the block is kept square.

FIG. 444.—3-litre Sports Chassis (1928). Back axle lay-out and lubrication points, and brake-adjusting rods.

The gear-box has three-point suspension, and provision is made for obtaining correct alignment, also the speedometer is driven from the gear-box. The gear-boxes fitted as standard to the speed and to the standard chassis are not the same. What Bentley's term the type " A " box is fitted on cars where only light sporting bodies are provided and the highest road speed is required under various conditions; this has a comparatively high first speed and only a small difference in ratio between second speed, third speed, and top. The " B " type box is fitted to the standard long chassis, with its first speed low and in the nature of an emergency gear, while the ratios are at much wider intervals between second, third, and top, as it is expected that these chassis will carry larger and heavier bodies.

There is nothing very special to worry about if the gear-box has to be dismantled, so no lengthy description of this process is given.

It may be necessary, however, to change a clutch cone and ring, and these parts can always be obtained from the manufacturers ready for fitting, without delay, so that no bedding in is required. In order to perform the work, remove the clutch shaft complete, and remove the ring bolted to the fly-wheel and withdraw the clutch cone from spigot. This is a job which requires a certain amount of care, in order that the spigot bearing may clear the clutch cross-shaft. When replacing, a block of wood should be placed between the withdrawal rollers and the end of the clutch spigot bearing, so as to take the thrust off the clutch spring, while the clutch is being secured in position by means of the eight bolts already referred to in the description of the clutch.

Should clutch slip occur, first make sure that there is about $\frac{1}{4}$ in. clearance between the clutch pedal and the front floor boards at the point where the pedal comes through the boards. If the floor boards are pressing on the pedal when the clutch is home, slip is bound to develop. A new car should, in particular, be watched for this, as the Ferodo lining beds in after a little mileage, and consequently the pedal comes further back.

If there is no clearance, remove the boards. At the base of the clutch pedal are two rollers, which bear against the clutch thrust race. These are mounted on eccentrics, and by undoing the nut and turning the eccentrics it is possible to give the pedal more clearance.

If this does not cure the clutch slip, or rather should this not be the cause of the slip, wedge the clutch pedal up. On the outside flange of the fly-wheel are the eight nuts which hold the clutch ring in position; undo these and draw off the ring. This then allows a clear view of the clutch lining. If greasy, it should be washed off with petrol and then roughed up with a coarse file.

As far as the transmission is concerned, the only item which requires some instruction to the repairer is in regard to the propeller shaft, which has a universal joint coupling immediately behind the gear-box of the ordinary star type and a pot joint at its rear end. The purpose of the pot joint is to allow for the plunging action of the back axle when the car is travelling over an uneven road. It is composed of a cross-head, fitted with phosphor bronze blocks, which move in slipper pieces, which are free to slide in steel guides. This joint is also fitted with an oil-tight cover, having an annular space round the propeller shaft. Just in front of this space, and bolted round the shaft, is a flange about 3 in. in diameter. The reason that this is fitted is in order to prevent grit and dust finding its way into the pot joint.

All engines have to have their tappets adjusted from time to time, and repairers and mechanics should note that up to and including engine No. 222 of the Bentley 3-litre model, the tappets should be adjusted by turning the fly-wheel until the line marked 1 and 4 is at the top. Get No. 1 cylinder on the firing stroke and set the tappets to ·015 in. Then turn the engine until mark 2 and 3 is at the top of the fly-wheel, that is, half a revolution. Make No. 3 ready for adjustment and after that No. 4, bearing in mind that No. 1 cylinder is nearest to the radiator.

For Bentley 3-litre engines, No. 223 onwards, carry out above instructions, but adjust inlet tappets to ·004 in. clearance and exhaust to ·006 in. when hot.

Tappets should be adjusted only when the engine is thoroughly warm.

Also tappet adjustments should be carried out on a new car after about 1,500 miles.

On the 1926 speed model and special speed model, and those cars which have been converted to the 1926 speed model modifications, the tappets should be adjusted to a clearance of ·019 in. The feeler gauge supplied in the tool kit for this purpose is marked 50, which really represents ·5 mm., which is approximately ·019 in. On the standard long chassis and light tourer engine, the adjustments remain at ·004 in. inlet and ·006 in. exhaust.

If at any time the rake of the steering requires altering, the only thing to be careful about is to put in a wedge-shaped packing piece between the steering column bracket and the dashboard, if the angle is altered to any considerable extent. Further, it must be remembered that altering the rake of the column necessitates the adjustment of the magneto controls. To do this, set the hand lever fully advanced on

Fig. 445.—Six-Cylinder Bentley Engine Complete (1928), showing near-side, also hot-air control, on left of carburettor, and front spring stop immediately behind rear shackle of front spring. Thermostat valve is fitted to the cooling system of this engine.

top of the steering column; at the bottom of the latter is a short rod, which is attached to a single lever on the magneto control cross-rod. Undo the pinch bolt on this lever and push both magnetos fully advanced, then tighten up again. By this method it is impossible to interfere with the synchronisation of the magnetos when performing this work of alteration of the steering rake.

To adjust the thermostat, which is situated on the exhaust side of the engine at the forward end of the copper water pipe above the exhaust manifold, unscrew the cover on which is a hexagonal boss. The valve, which is secured on its

Fig. 446.—Six-Cylinder Bentley (1928), showing back view of front wheel lock and tie-rod adjustment A and lubrication points.

spindle by a split pin, will then be seen. Remove the split pin, and to make the engine run cooler, unscrew the valve three-quarters or a complete turn. Replace the split pin and cover. The correct working temperature of the engine is from 75° to 80° C. or 167° to 176° F., and the engine under ordinary conditions should run consistently at this temperature.

Four wheel brakes were introduced as standard on all Bentley chassis about September 1923. These brakes are of the mechanical type operated by the brake pedal; independent brakes on the rear drums only are operated by the hand brake lever. If one side or one shoe on the two wheel brakes continually rubs on the drum when the car is in motion, it is necessary to alter the compensation. To do this proceed as follows, viz.: with the help of the special hub extractors provided in the tool kit, having first removed the split pin and nut of the hubs, slacken off the brake, remove pull-off springs, and then the shoes. Next undo the pinch bolts which clamp the brake levers on to the brake camshafts. The brake camshaft operates the shoes, forcing them apart when the brake is applied. Remove the brake levers, taking care not to lose the keys for same, which are in the camshaft. Now make quite certain that the camshafts are quite free to rotate not only together, but also one inside the other. If they are not free, remove them by pulling them out and ease them down with emery cloth. Having got the camshaft free, replace the levers, taking care not to have the outside lever too close to the inside lever, as if this happens they bind together on the bush separating them. Next assemble the shoes and tighten the springs up equally. Replace the drums temporarily, jack up both back wheels, also chock the front wheels to prevent the car falling off the jacks. On no account should only one rear wheel be jacked up and the engine run with the gear in mesh, as this procedure might cause damage to the rear axle.

Then run the engine, engage top gear and apply the brake until you can hear the brake lining in contact with the drum. If one side comes on first, remove the drum and tighten up the springs about two turns on each spring; replace drums and run again. Whichever side comes on first indicates that the springs are weakest on that side. Whilst screwing up the eye bolts, which hold the brake springs, when starting to compensate the brakes, it is advisable to have about half the thread protruding through the nut, as this makes sure that there is sufficient tension on the spring at the start of operations to ensure the shoes coming away from the drums when the brake is released.

To rectify a scraping sound in brakes when cornering, caused by the dust cover generally, which is over the inside

FIG. 447.—Front View Chassis, 4½-litre Bentley (1928).

of the brake drum, rubbing on the brake drum itself, this dust cover should be eased back with a big screw-driver, or knocked back with a hammer.

A balance gear is fitted to ensure that the braking effect is distributed evenly on all four brake drums. This is mounted across the frame immediately behind the gear-box; its valuable feature is that friction is utilised to ensure that the brakes release together. When the balance gear has been correctly adjusted in the first place, no further attention is required by it for a very great mileage. To take up wear only one adjustment is necessary, and that is to be found under the front to the rear of the lower end of the brake pedal. The adjustment for the hand brake is on the outside of the chassis frame at the lower end of the brake lever.

To adjust the Smith-Bentley carburettor, it is necessary to examine the jets and disconnect the petrol pipe beneath the float chamber. Underneath the arm that carries the float chamber will be found a nut; undo this nut, and the float chamber, complete with jet platform, can be dropped. The jets are numbered 1 to 4, these numbers being stamped on the jet platform. Between this group of four jets and the float chamber is another jet called the well jet, which supplies the petrol to the engine for slow running and starting. After the engine has been started, the other jets come into action in succession. The makers claim that after running a new car 2,000 to 3,000 miles, the well jet may probably be cut down without detrimentally affecting the running of the engine. Likewise Nos. 1 and 2 jets may be cut down; but whether smaller jets can be advantageously fitted can only be determined by experiment.

The following are the standard and possible experimental jet sizes, viz. :—

	Standard.	Experimental.
Well jet	45	40
No. 1	45	42
No. 2	75	72
No. 3	50	50
No. 4	35	35

The experimental sizes are merely suggestions, and the mechanic must use his own judgment as to whether there is any improved running as a result of the alterations.

The dashpot is situated above the jets and can be removed, the jet block having been dropped, by undoing four small nuts on the underside of the carburettor body. The dashpot rises up and down the port block, thereby uncovering the jets successively, according to the engine revolutions and the throttle opening. The writer has found from personal experience that this dashpot sometimes works better when cleaned and polished with any liquid metal polish, so that there is as little friction in its action as possible.

FIG. 448.—$4\frac{1}{2}$-litre Bentley Engine (1928), showing oil filter partly dismantled, also the oil-level gauge, starting handle holding clip on right of oil gauge.

The air control knob on the switch plate should be pushed in for starting from cold. This has the effect of giving a rich mixture, a cowl being raised round the well jet, cutting off the air supply. This control knob should not be left in the rich position for longer than is absolutely necessary, as sooting up the plugs will result. The control should be pulled out to the normal running position, it being located there by the spring-loaded ball catch. After the engine has warmed up, the control can be pulled out still further; but the best running position can only be decided by actual practice.

SIX-CYLINDER BENTLEY

The engine of the six-cylinder Bentley has a cubic capacity of 6,597 c.c. and an R.A.C. rating of 37·2 H.P. The oil capacity of the sump is 3 gals., and lubrication is by a pressure pump for main and big end bearings and overhead gear, splash to pistons and gudgeon pins, while the cooling is by the ordinary pump water circulation and fan. Boil ignition and one M.L. magneto are fitted for the dual ignition, and a special Smith-Bentley carburettor; while the 25-gal. rear fuel tank feeds the autovac. Twelve K.L.G. sparking plugs, type J. 1, are provided, four overhead valves are fitted per cylinder (two inlet and two exhaust), the crankshaft has eight bearings, as likewise has the camshaft, while aluminium B.H.B. pinions are fitted. The electrical batteries are specially designed and manufactured by Messrs Peto & Radford. Semi-balloon tyres, 33 × 6·75 in., are fitted on Rudge-Whitworth detachable wire wheels. The clutch is a single dry plate, the gear-box has four speeds forward and a reverse; whilst Dewandre foot brake operating on all four wheels, together with a hand brake acting in separate shoes to the rear wheels only, are the braking controls.

The valves of the engine are operated by duralumin rockers, having at one end a hardened steel roller which bears on the camshaft, and at the other end a ball-ended tappet which depresses the valve. The tappet screw is secured by a lock-nut, and the tappets can be simply adjusted.

To adjust the tappets, the aluminium cam-case cover is held in position by ten stainless steel nuts which must be unscrewed, after which the cover can be lifted off. Should it have stuck, it can be started by inserting a screw-driver into the four recesses provided for the purpose and gently levering it up. Care must be taken not to damage the cork washer which makes the joint between the cover and the cam-case. The two aluminium side plates, each secured by seven nuts, can then be removed; but before commencing adjustments, the engine must be thoroughly hot. Each tappet screw is secured by a lock-nut, to fit which a ring spanner is supplied

Fig. 449.—Six-Cylinder Bentley Engine (1928). Carburettor side top removed, showing tappet adjusting spanners in position on No. 1 cylinder, showing carburettor, also hot-air control for carburettor. Oil filler (B) autovac with visible petrol filter, starting handle as permanently carried on dash under bonnet, also four spare sparking plugs, as well as magneto.

in the tool kit, together with a key into the end of the tappet screw, thereby affording means of adjusting the clearance between the ball end of the tappet screw and the end of the valve stem.

The order of firing of the cylinders is 1, 4, 2, 6, 3, 5, No. 1 being the front cylinder near the radiator. As the tappets are adjusted for each individual cylinder, that cylinder must be at top dead centre on the firing stroke, this position being marked on the fly-wheel. For instance, when adjusting No. 1 cylinder, the marks T.D.C. 1 and 6 on the fly-wheel must be in line with the centre of the cylinder block, the actual cylinder which is on the firing stroke being ascertained by inspecting the position of the magneto distributor.

The correct clearances are ·004 in. on the inlet and ·006 in.

Fig. 450.—Bentley Six-Cylinder Engine Complete (1928). Hot Water Jacketed Carburettor, showing hot-air control, magneto, autovac and filter, oil filler and front wheel spring stop.

on the exhaust side. It must be realised that the ball end of the tappet screws is free to rotate, so that care must be exercised when adjusting that the flats on the balls bear on the valve stems. After adjusting and tightening up the lock-nut, the clearances should be finally checked. When replacing the side plates and cover, the nuts must be tightened up evenly, and in no circumstances must any joint material be used apart from the washers.

One might mention here, that should a squeak develop in

the overhead gear after the engine has been standing by unused for a considerable period, it is probably due to a dry or rusty tappet screw ball, and it is these parts which should be investigated with a view to curing that trouble, though the noise will automatically wear off in use.

The B.H.B. aluminium pistons are each fitted with three rings and a scraper ring all at the crown.

FIG. 451.—Six-Cylinder Bentley Engine Complete (1928). Exhaust side, showing coil ignition, hot-air gauzes, thermostat in cooling system, front spring stop, and steering arm and rod.

It will be noticed two priming cocks are mounted on top of the induction manifold; but they are only placed there as a standby for the owner, as a Ki-gass primer is fitted as standard equipment in order to give an easy start from cold. This Ki-gass petrol injector consists of a plunger pump fitted in the instrument board with pipes connecting it to the top of the induction pipe and to the main fuel supply of the carburettor, as illustrated by Fig. 450. The pump plunger, on being unscrewed to put it in action and withdrawn, draws a pumpful of fuel from the main fuel supply pipe, and on

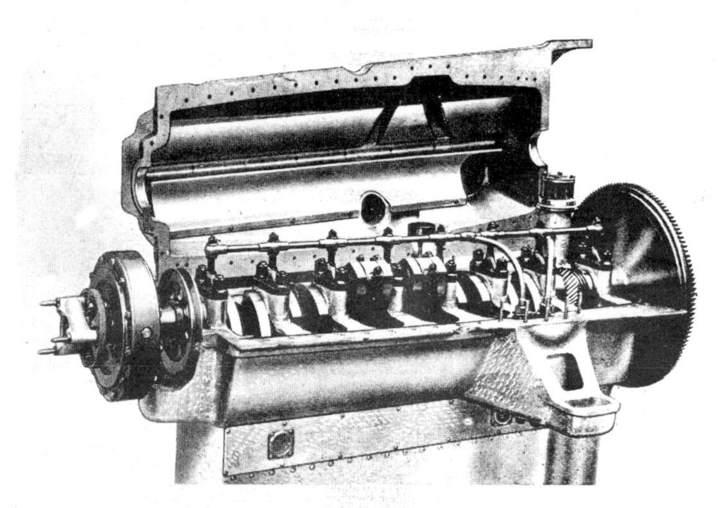

Fig. 452.—Six-Cylinder Bentley Engine (1928), upside down with sump off, showing oil pipes, oil pump, and method of driving dynamo by three spigots (extreme left of picture).

Fig. 453.—Bentley Six-Cylinder Model (1928), showing clutch and stop, gear-box, universal joint and servo brake box, speedometer drive and revolution counter.

being pushed in, the fuel is forced in a vaporised form into the induction pipe in two places. When the engine is to be started, this plunger is withdrawn and pushed in three times, then screwed home, and it is only because of this latter qualification that it is mentioned in this narrative. This screwing home is most important, as, if left unscrewed, neat fuel will be drawn into the induction pipe through the Ki-gass connections immediately the engine starts, thus making the mixture over-rich. If at any time the engine is dismantled,

FIG. 454.—Six-Cylinder Bentley (1928) Back Axle Lay-out, showing lubrication points. Note curved exhaust pipe from silencer to clear back axle casing when rear springs are flexed.

it will be noticed that the big end bearings have no brasses, the white metal being secured direct into the connecting rod end. This has been done to keep down weight.

To adjust the clutch stop, which consists of a metal ring mounted on the rear side of the Hardy disc on the clutch shaft, it is necessary occasionally after long periods to take up the wear on the halo pad. A spring plate is anchored at one end to a bracket on the front nose-piece of the gear-box. The other end is connected by a link to a point on the clutch pedal arm, a few inches from its lower end. Mounted on the spring plate is a pad of halo. As the clutch pedal is pushed forward, this pad is pressed against the metal ring, acting as a brake on the clutch shaft. The degree of fierceness of this stop is adjustable by turning the knurled hand wheel, which forms part of the link mentioned above, having first loosened the lock-nut securing it. A coil spring is contained in the barrel, which is an extension of the knurled hand wheel, and the link expands against the pressure of this spring as the clutch pedal is pushed forward, increasing the pressure of the pad on the ring. This avoids making the stop too definite in action. The stop is adjusted to be light in action when the chassis leaves the works, but drivers can adjust it to suit their individual tastes.

THE 4½-LITRE BENTLEY

Four valves are used in each cylinder—two inlet and two exhaust—in the 4½-litre Bentley, because by using two valves instead of one, the seating area is increased by 50 per cent., and in consequence the cooling surface is greater, while a greater volume of water can be circulated through the space surrounding the seatings. Further, as silence is one of the qualities demanded nowadays by the modern motorist, the hammering effect on the seating of a single large valve with a heavy spring is greatly diminished by using two light valves with correspondingly lighter springs. As far as the upkeep of the car is concerned, the repairer will find that he has no more to do on this than on the 3-litre model, and the 4½-litre Bentley usually runs about 20,000 miles before there is any need for regrinding valves and seatings. Practically the chassis is an enlarged edition of the 3-litre, so that what is required to be done for one has in due course, when necessary, to be done for the other.

There are two magnetos and two sets of plugs, so it is actually dual ignition, as the engine can run with only one set going, though both magnetos are synchronised, and the timing is just as easy to set as on the other models, the same method being employed. What one has to remember is that there is a separate switch provided for each magneto,

FIG. 455.—$4\frac{1}{2}$-litre Bentley Engine (1928), with valve cover removed for tappet adjustment. See spanner and key in position, two S.U. carburettors, showing off-side magneto. (Second magneto is in the same position on the near-side.)

FIG. 456.—$4\frac{1}{2}$-litre Bentley Engine (1928), showing sump removed, also pump gear and oil leads. In the upper picture the oil-level gauge is shown on the aluminium base plate and the eight gauze squares of the sump filter. Note that the base chamber has been turned upside down in order to show its details more clearly.

so as to test each set of plugs, and it sometimes is necessary to see that the switch wires are all right.

The special twin S.U. carburettors with variable mixture control are provided, and the petrol tank carried in the rear holds 16 gals., and is fitted with Hobson's "Telegage" petrol level gauge, with the dial fitted to the instrument board, showing the amount of fuel available in the tank. It must be remembered, however, that usually about three parts of a quart never show on the gauge, and neither will the

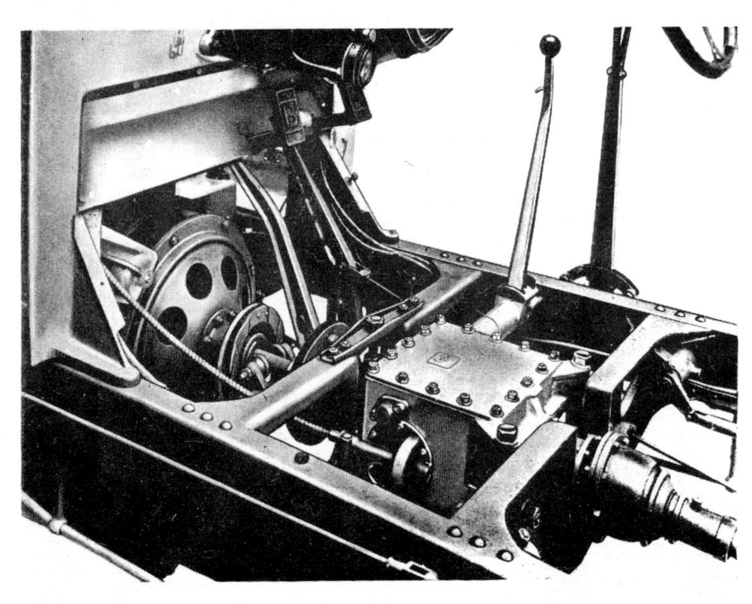

FIG. 457.—$4\frac{1}{2}$-litre Bentley (1928), showing clutch gear-box and universal joint lay-out, revolving counter and speedometer drive, leaf spring clutch stop.

autovac system lift that amount of the tank, which has deceived many a motorist on all makes of cars using autovacs, as they all have this same peculiarity.

In servicing this car it has to be remembered that there are only three grease cups on the chassis; all other parts are provided with Tecalemit connections through which they can be loaded by means of an oil gun. The makers state that after this chassis has been lubricated, it can be run for three months of normal mileage without further lubrication, apart from the engine requirements, and as owners are liable to take advantage of this, when a chassis does come in for lubrication, it must be thoroughly well attended to. Some Bentleys have the ordinary Perrot type of four wheel brakes,

FIG. 458.—$4\frac{1}{2}$-litre Bentley (1928), showing lay-out of rear wheel brakes with drum cover removed, displaying double brake bands; the inside band is made of cast iron for hand brake shoes. Outside band (dark), wood fibre for foot brake shoes, together with shock absorbers, filler cap, and method of supporting petrol tank.

while others have the vacuum or Dewandre system added thereto to increase the braking power; but, in either case, servicing is no different from what has already been described.

A brief specification of the $4\frac{1}{2}$-litre Bentley, rated at 24·8 H.P. for its four cylinders of 100×140 mm., giving a total capacity of 4,398·24 c.c., is given here, as the model is so new that few have come into general hands, and therefore the details are comparatively unknown :—

Size of tyres	$32\frac{1}{2} \times 5\frac{1}{4}$ in. to fit 21-in. rims.
Wheel base	10 ft. 10 in.
Width of frame at cross-members . .	2 ft. 11 in.
Width of frame at second cross-member .	2 ft. $8\frac{1}{4}$ in.
Overall width	5 ft. $8\frac{1}{2}$ in.
Overall length	14 ft. $4\frac{1}{2}$ in.
Ground clearance with $32\frac{1}{2}$-in. tyres .	$7\frac{3}{4}$ in.
Weight of chassis	25 cwt.
Body space from dash to rear cross-rail of body	8 ft.
Maximum weight of complete car permissible under makers' guarantee . . .	$33\frac{1}{2}$ cwt.

N.B.—Coachbuilders should note this last restriction, as all chassis are sold with and subject to the Bentley Company's five-year guarantee.

Fig. 459.—$4\frac{1}{2}$-litre Bentley Back Axle (1928), showing oil filler for differential casing, petrol filler at side, and rear brake adjustments and Tecalemit oilers.

Valve timing and diagrams for the four Bentley models are as under:—

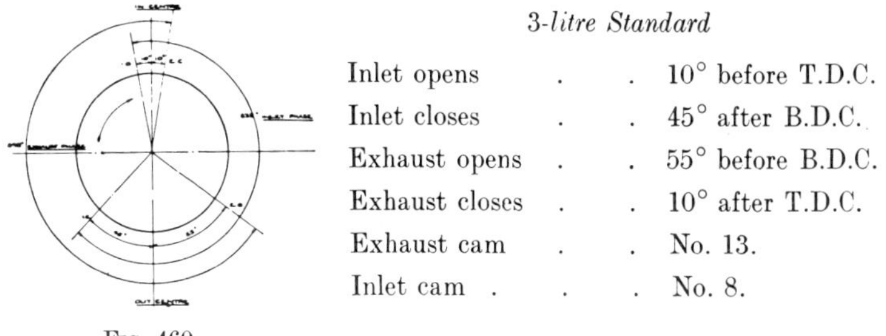

Fig. 460.

3-litre Standard

Inlet opens . .	10° before T.D.C.
Inlet closes . .	45° after B.D.C.
Exhaust opens . .	55° before B.D.C.
Exhaust closes . .	10° after T.D.C.
Exhaust cam . .	No. 13.
Inlet cam . . .	No. 8.

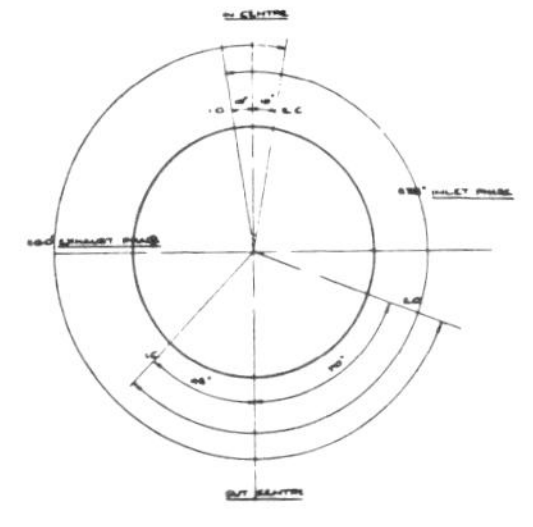

Fig. 461.

3-litre Sports and 4½-litre

Inlet opens . .	10° before T.D.C.
Inlet closes . .	45° after B.D.C.
Exhaust opens . .	70° before B.D.C.
Exhaust closes . .	10° after T.D.C.
Exhaust cam . .	No. 7.
Inlet cam . . .	No. 8.

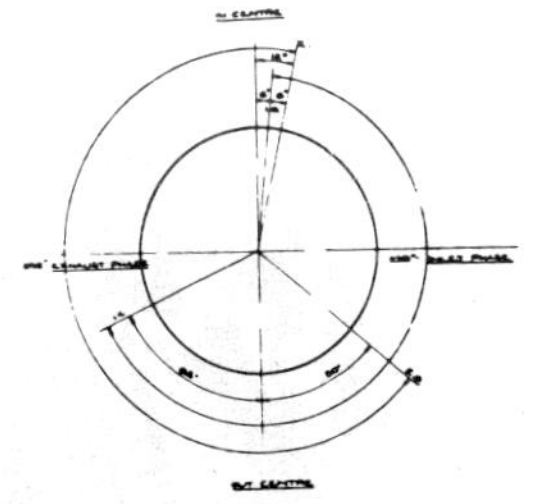

Fig. 462.

Six-Cylinder

Inlet opens . .	6° before T.D.C.
Inlet closes . .	65° after B.D.C.
Exhaust opens . .	50° before B.D.C.
Exhaust closes . .	12° after T.D.C.

Firing order, 1, 4, 2, 6, 3, 5.

Firing order of all four-cylinder Bentley models is 1, 3, 4, 2.

BUGATTI

FOUR AND EIGHT CYLINDER CARS

A MAKE of French car particularly well known to the racing world is the Bugatti, made at Molsheim, Bas-Rhin, France. This car is made in eleven models, three of four and eight of eight cylinders, all with overhead valves and overhead camshaft, having two inlet and one exhaust valve for each cylinder. In the four-cylinder models, Nos. 37 and 40, the four cylinders are cast *en bloc* and have a bore of 69 mm. and a stroke of 100 mm. The eight-cylinder models are cast in pairs.

The following are the current productions :—

TOURING

4-cylinder,	1,500 c.c.	11·9	H.P.	British	rating.	
8 ,,	2-litre	17·8	,,	,,	,,	
8 ,,	3-litre	23·6	,,	,,	,,	
8 ,,	2,300 c.c.	17·8	,,	,,	,,	supercharged.

The Grand Prix range consists of the following :—

4-cylinder	1,500 c.c.	11·9	H.P.	British	rating,	unsupercharged.
4 ,,	,, ,,	,,	,,	,,	,,	supercharged.
8 ,,	,, ,,	,,	,,	,,	,,	unsupercharged.
8 ,,	,, ,,	,,	,,	,,	,,	supercharged.
8 ,,	2-litre	17·8	,,	,,	,,	unsupercharged.
8 ,,	2,300 c.c.	,,	,,	,,	,,	unsupercharged.
8 ,,	,, ,,	,,	,,	,,	,,	supercharged.

On all present-day models constructional features, and consequently servicing details, are common to all chassis. In the four-cylinder models, the types 37 and 40 have the cylinders cast *en bloc*, the bore and stroke being 69 × 100 mm. ; but in types 35A, 35, 43, and 44 the cylinders are cast in pairs, the bore and stroke of the 35A and 35 being 60 × 88 mm., whilst type 43 is 60 × 100 mm., and type 44 is 69 × 100 mm. respectively.

Types 40, 43, 45, and 47 have five bearings for the crankshaft; type 38 has three, and type 44 nine.

Other differences of the models are that the petrol feed of types 38, 40, and 44 is by vacuum, but type 43 and the three Grand Prix models, viz., 35A, 35, and 37, have pressure feed; types 38 and 40 and the Grand Prix models have Solex carburettors, the eight-cylinder models having two carburettors, whilst type 43 is fitted with a Zenith triple diffuser carburettor, whereas type 44 is fitted with a Schebler. Type 43 is fitted with a supercharger. Type 37 can be fitted with a supercharger if required, but the standard model does not incorporate this.

Types 35 and 43 have magneto ignition, otherwise all have Delco coil. The gear-boxes are a separate unit and are fitted with central control with the exception of the three Grand Prix models, and these are right-hand control.

Types 40, 43, and 44 are fitted with a separate dynamo and starting motor; the type 38 is fitted with a combined unit. In all cases the dynamos are positively driven. There are no starters to the Grand Prix models, and on the full Grand Prix (racing type) 35 there is no electrical equipment at all outside the ignition.

All models are cooled by pump circulation, with forced feed lubrication by pressure gear type of pump. The smaller models have five crankshaft bearings and an automatic carburettor fed through vacuum auxiliary tank on the dash inside the bonnet. The larger models have three ball-bearing crankshaft bearings and two Solex carburettors, also fed through auxiliary tank like their smaller confrères. The ignition is by battery and distributor.

All models are fitted with Bugatti patent steel and cast-iron multiple disc type of clutch, and a four-speed and reverse gear-box with gate change, direct drive being on top gear. The steering is of the worm and helical wheel type, irreversible and adjustable with ball and socket connecting rods. The front springs are semi-elliptic and the rear quarter elliptic, anchored at the rear end of the chassis and extending forward to the rear axle. Brakes are pedal operated on all four wheels, whilst the hand lever operates the rear wheel drums only.

The water pump is placed at the right-hand side of the engine. It draws up the water from the base of the radiator and brings it into the cylinder block, which has an inlet tube on each side at the top, connected to the radiator. The circulation is arranged in such a manner that there is no need for a fan. This pump must be looked after. An automatic lubricator has been provided to grease its spindle, which

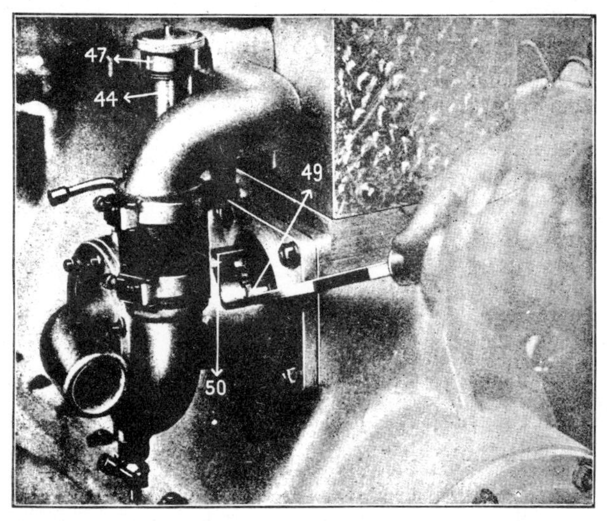

Fig. 518.—Showing Automatic Lubrication of Water Pump.

lubricator is composed of a fairly long cylinder (thus allowing a fair reserve of grease to be retained), of a piston, a spring, and a cap. Under the action of the spring pressure, the grease penetrates through the various parts of the pump and maintains it in good condition, so that it works well. The supply of grease is exhausted when the piston rod reaches within 1 cm. of the cap, as shown in Fig. 518. To refill this, proceed as shown in Fig. 519. It is necessary to first unscrew the cap, take out the spring and piston, and proceed to fill, as shown in Fig. 519, using a grease which is sufficiently thick to allow of it being made into a roll to permit it being introduced into the empty cylinder. On replacing the piston, spring, and cap, the piston rod then appears as shown in Fig. 520.

The tightness of the pump axis or spindle is assured by a close stuffing. If there is an escape of water at this spot, it is necessary to tighten up gland by screwing down a bronze milled screw to compress the packing. For this, all that is necessary is to insert a screw-driver in the notch on the screw and apply pressure on the handle to turn the screw ; continue to exercise this pressure until sufficient resistance is felt to

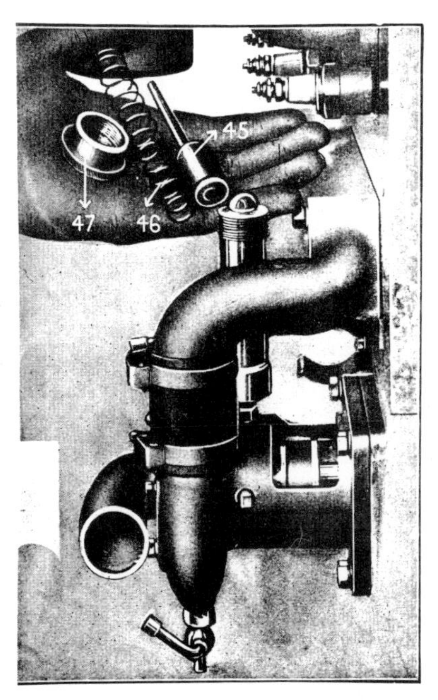

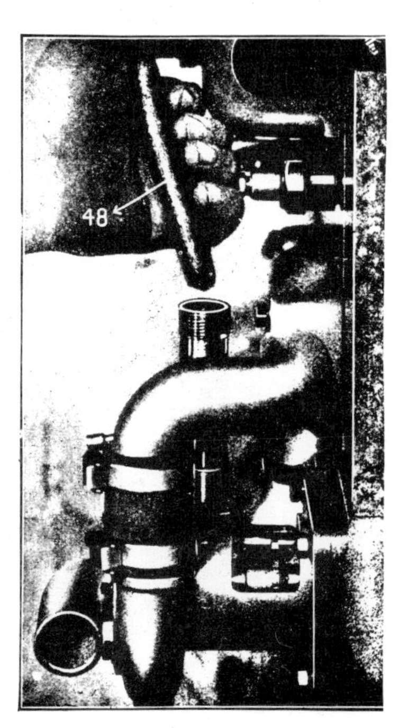

Fig. 519.—Showing Automatic Lubrication of Water Pump.

prove that the stuffing is tight enough to stop any leakage of water. No. 50 (Fig. 518) shows a spring which should fall into a notch on the gland to keep it fixed in the position in which it is placed. The chalky deposits in circulating water may lead to wear on the end of the pump axis or spindle, which is catered for by a screw at the centre of the pump. The position of this screw is fixed by a counter-screw nut engaged in the keyway. When the end is worn a little excessively, the turbine, which is of aluminium, can then rub against the body of the aluminium pump and can ruin it completely if it is not adjusted right away. This adjustment is essential, and is provided only for the eight-cylinder models. To adjust, it is necessary to unscrew the counter-screw nut and keep it unscrewed until the screw has been tightened up until it comes into contact with the axis or spindle of the pump, as shown in Fig. 520. Then rescrew up the counter-

Fig. 520.—Showing Automatic Lubrication of Water Pump.

screw nut. To accomplish this adjustment well, after the screw has come into contact with the extremity of the spindle, unscrew it one-sixth of a turn, then screw up the counter-screw nut. In order to avoid chalky deposits, it is better whenever possible to use distilled or rain water for the radiator.

The lubrication of the engine is the most important item. It is extremely simple, but should receive most careful attention, as it is certainly the basis of the good running and functioning of the whole vehicle. If the lubrication is neglected, either by the use of inferior oil or by lack of oil, from that time the engine will cease to function properly. In no circumstances should the engine be allowed to lack oil. Always see that the oil level is correct, as this is easily to be seen from the oil gauge. To put in oil it is necessary to raise the cover 52 in Fig. 521, put on the pipe 53, merely swinging aside the spring 54, shown in Fig. 522, and proceed as indicated in the illustration, watching the ascension on the gauge in order not to put in too much. One should wait a few minutes to give the oil time to pass through the filter placed at the lower part of the casing before it enters the sump. The oil circulation to the engine is assured by gear type of pump. The lower part of the casing forms a reservoir for the oil. The total capacity of the oil reservoir in the casing is about $1\frac{1}{4}$ gals. in all models, except type 44 ($1\frac{1}{2}$ gals.). This oil is partly in circulation in the engine during running, and the remainder is cooled by the current of air passing through the tubes which traverse the lower part of the casing. Moreover, these tubes considerably augment the cooling surface. Oil is drawn into the pump, which forces it back into the filter; under the effect of the pressure the oil is forced to the main bearings. Other connections carry the oil into the channels, where by centrifugal force it is supplied to the friction surfaces of the connecting rods. The cylinders and pistons are lubricated by splash. At the extreme end of

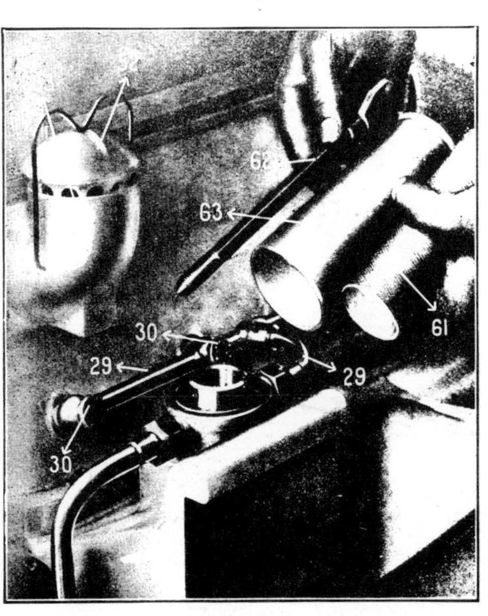

Fig. 521.—Showing Details of Replenishment of Oil in Crank-Case and Position of Oil Filter.

the tube running from the filter to the different lubricating points, there is a pipe which branches off and distributes the oil at two points for the lubrication of the camshaft and the valves, etc. All oil which is not used and which escapes from the connecting rods, etc., is taken back to the casing after passing through the filter, which extends over the whole length of the casing. There are two filters, and the one being very fine needs to be cleaned very frequently, which should be done by taking out and washing with benzol or petrol. If the filter happens to be very dirty and caked, it will be necessary to scratch with the fingers. Also, at the same time, clean the inside of the casing.

Fig. 522.—Showing Details of Replenishment of Oil in Crank-Case and Position of Oil Filter.

For the first 3,000 miles approximately of running, it is necessary to empty the oil out of the engine about every 500 to 600 miles, and thereafter about every 3,000 miles or so. To do this it is merely necessary to take off the cap at the bottom of the casing. Be careful to screw the cap on tightly again after refilling. Never wash the engine with petrol after emptying. Refill exactly as previously described.

In regard to the lubrication of steering pins on Bugatti cars, it is as well to mention that on the top of the steering pin is a small oil hole. Oil is used and not grease, and to get at this hole it is necessary to push to one side the pulley carrying the brake cable, otherwise it is apt to be neglected, and it is most important that this should be attended to, as it is slightly different from the usual practice on other makes of cars.

The clutch, as previously mentioned, is of the multiple disc cast-iron and steel type, completely enclosed in the fly-wheel and in a tight manner, so that this permits of its working in a mixture of lubricant composed of half oil and half paraffin in summer (a little less should be used in winter). The clutch should be washed and greased as frequently as

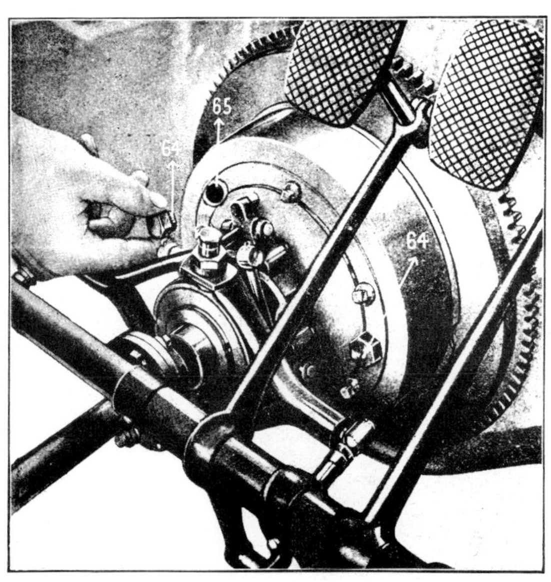

FIG. 523.—Showing Lubrication of Clutch.

possible. For this purpose, unscrew one of the two nuts 64 (Fig. 523), turn the fly-wheel to get the hole at the bottom, and the lubricant will run out, taking the deposits with it. It is as well to inject petrol with a syringe to wash the discs and then empty out again. Then refill with lubricant, half oil and half paraffin, by placing the hole, as indicated in Fig. 523, level with the horizontal axis, and the lubricant is correct when it reaches the height of the nut hole. The clutch works quite well without much pressure on the pedal to declutch, but a good pressure is necessary to separate all the discs one from the other. Adjustment is provided for any slight wear. Fig. 524 represents the position of declutching. No. 70 shows the screw which allows of the adjustment. For this, all that is necessary is to insert a cylindrical bar into one of the nut holes, which bar must be of the same diameter as the hole, and apply pressure on the pedal to maintain the declutching, then turn towards the right. Turn only one notch at a time and try the adjustment by letting the pedal go back. When the rods 69 (Fig. 525) can be brought into line with each other by a slight pressure, the adjustment is correct. If on sharply

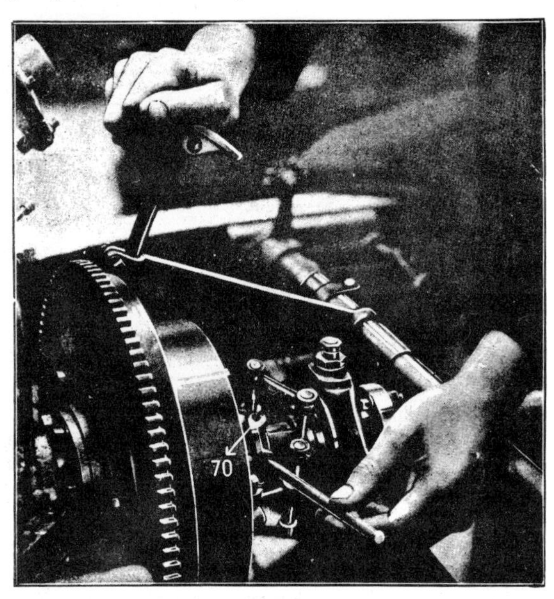

FIG. 524.—Clutch Withdrawn for Purposes of Adjustment by means of Nut 17.

releasing the pedal these rods do not come in line, the adjustment is too tight ; it is necessary in this case to turn back a notch.

The point indicated by No. 163 (Fig. 526) should be frequently lubricated if the car is run much in places where it is necessary to declutch often. Besides this small end, there is a little end piece which limits the advancement of the clutch adjusting nut up to $\frac{8}{10}$ mm. In the four-cylinder models this adjustment can be made by means of adjusting the nut right and left on the driving rod (tringle rod) of the fork ; in the eight cylinders by means of a screw and counter-screw nut placed below.

The gear-box casing is in one piece with a cover, on which is mounted the control lever and the gate for the different speeds. To test the lubrication of the gear-box it is only necessary to unscrew all the nuts which fix the cover, which permits of taking it out complete. The oil level should reach the lower part of the shaft. Every 6,000 or 7,000 miles the gear-box should be emptied and refilled. Thick oil should be used, but never heavy grease. Before refilling, one should very carefully wash the bottom of the casing with petrol. Never use a rag, only a brush.

Fig. 525.—Another View of Clutch, showing Adjustment of Clutch Withdrawal Gear.

Fig. 526.—Lubrication of Clutch Ball Thrust Bearing.

On each side of the chassis a cable joins the control lever of the front brake to that of the rear brake. The hand brake lever, of course, only operates on the rear, but the pedal acts on all four wheels. At the middle of the cable on each side of the vehicle is a chain, the front of which is terminated by a threaded rod (No. 162, Fig. 527), which allows of the shortening of the cable. The chain engages on the pinions 135, shown in the illustration, the lower two being mounted on the frame member, whereas the one above in each instance is mounted on an axis at the end of the lever.

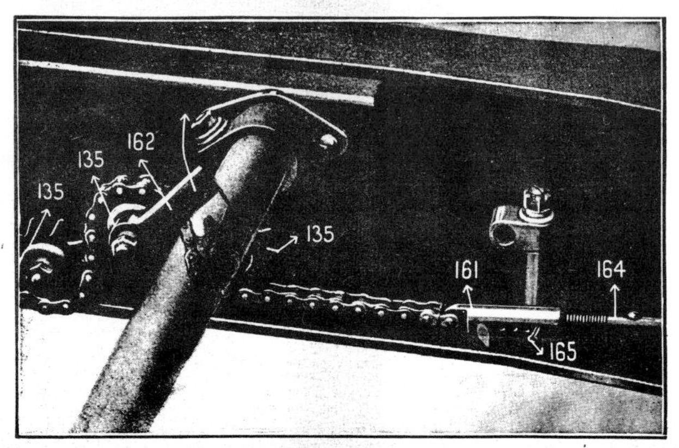

FIG. 527.—Brake Cable Adjustment.

FIG. 528.—Means adopted for Lubrication of Pulley on which the Brake Cables Run.

The pressure exerted in the two cables is equalised on the two sets of wheels and is compensated. The equalisation is not affected by any undue stress or conditions of running.

Actually the brakes should not need much adjustment, but if the reader will refer to Fig. 527 there will be no difficulty in seeing just how to shorten the cable by means of the pin

165, but care should be taken to see that this is properly fixed in. In order to screw down the screw 164 it is necessary to release the cable from the lower pulley in box 99, shown on Fig. 528, lifting the cover 100, shown in the same figure, and unhook the extreme end of the cable, shown in Fig. 529, No. 167, by means of the opening E. This adjustment merely serves to recover the correct length of the cable; it should be drawn very lightly slack, the pedal being at rest. The brake cable holding rod should also be left slack, as shown in Fig. 530, which shows the best position, and under no condition should this key or rod be drawn up tight, as shown in Fig. 529, which illustrates a very bad position.

Fig. 529.—Brake Cable Adjustment.

Fig. 530.—Brake Cable Adjustment.

To adjust the rear wheel brakes proceed as follows:—

Unscrew the two nuts 159 and the two screws 160, as shown in Fig. 531, by two turns. Inside the axle tube 158, shown in Fig. 532, is the driving shaft, which terminates in a cone on which is mounted the wheel hub which supports the brake drum. The wheel must be removed. To do this, take off the nut at the end of the

FIG. 531.—Brake Drums and their Adjustment.

interior shaft, then by means of a wheel drawer screwed on the wheel hub it is easy to take out the drum, as shown in Fig. 531. Withdraw the drum completely. It is then necessary to place steel wedges under the jaws, as shown in Fig. 533, No. 166. This wedge should be of a minimum thickness of 1·5 mm. so that it shall not be bent, and should be firmly fixed to each jaw. Before definitely fixing the wedge it is essential to try wedges of different thicknesses until the correct one is found. Be careful to wedge the two jaws in each drum equally. To try out each thickness of wedge, remount the brake drum, and manœuvre the brake rod, which should move lightly. In some cases it is permissible to slightly file the jaw carrier so that a wedge of sufficient thickness can be inserted. Then it is essential to ascertain that these jaws bear evenly all over the surface and over all the periphery, and for that

FIG. 532.—Brake Drums and their Adjustment.

purpose it is sufficient to put a little chalk on the inside of the brake drum. When braking, the chalk will then leave traces on the jaws showing the places which touch. This job should never be done by anyone who is not thoroughly qualified to do it most carefully. The front wheel brakes are adjusted

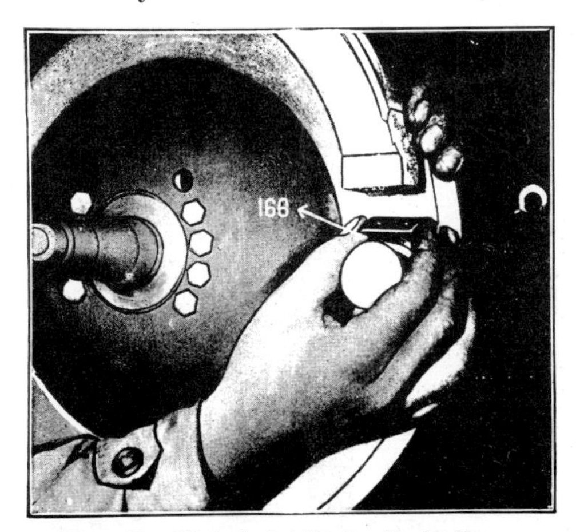

FIG. 533.—Method of Adjusting Brake Shoes.

FIG. 534.—Showing Overhead Valve Adjustment.

in the same manner after having withdrawn the hub with the wheel drawer. To replace, it is sufficient to replace the hub on the cone, making sure that the key exactly enters its keyway and that the nut is properly tightened in its place.

The valves are operated by a camshaft, which is driven by two pinions or gear wheels 144 and 145 (Fig. 535). It is supported by a rod between each group of three cams. Tubes 152 cross the camshaft casing along its whole length at each side, and one supports the inlet rockers and the other supports the exhaust rockers and nuts, and screws 141 hold the rockers in position.

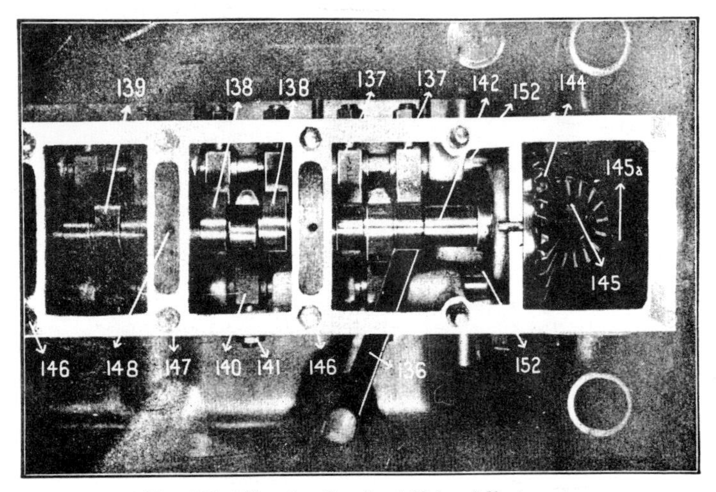

Fig. 535.—Showing Overhead Valve Adjustment.

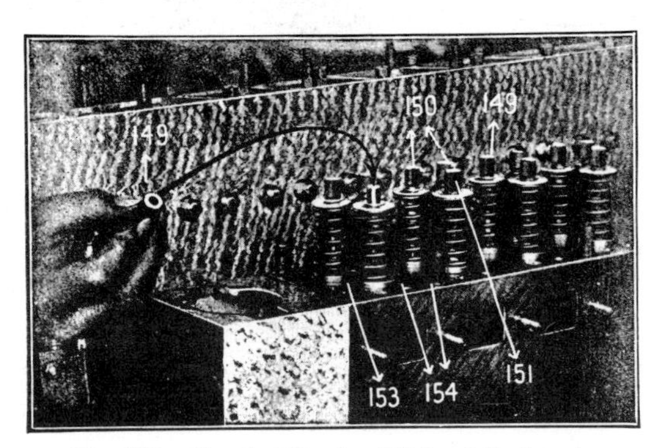

Fig. 536.—Showing Overhead Valve Adjustment.

Fig. 536 shows the camshaft casing with the cams lifted. For this it is enough to unscrew the nuts 146, of which the threaded ends are introduced into the studs (153, Fig. 536). These studs serve to fix the camshaft casing cover. In Fig. 536 the hand is holding the cap from the valve marked by an arrow. Each valve has a similar cap. According to the thickness of the base of this cap, the play between the rocker and the cam can be varied; this is where the adjustment is provided. If there is too much play, the cap must be changed for one of a thicker base; on the contrary, if there is not sufficient play, then the cap must be changed for one with a thinner base. The necessary play is shown in Figs. 537 and 538, according to the numbers of the engine. To verify the

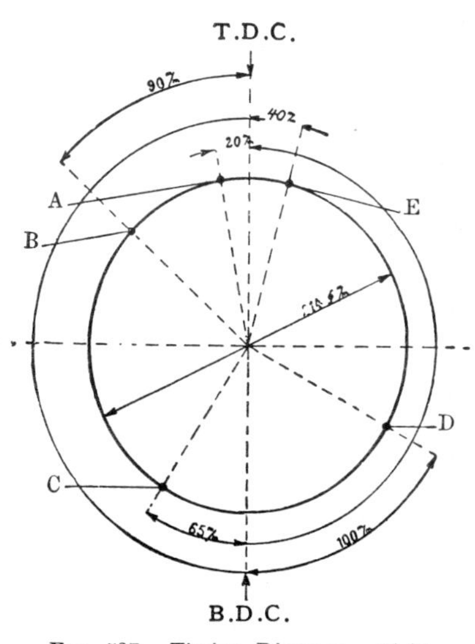

Fig. 537.—Timing Diagram. 1½-litre Model 37, Four-Cylinder.

A, Inlet opens.
B, Maximum ignition advance.
C, Inlet closes.
D, Exhaust opens.
E, Exhaust closes.

Tappet clearance for inlet and exhaust, ·75 mm. = ·028 in.
Order of firing of cylinders, 1, 2, 4, 3.

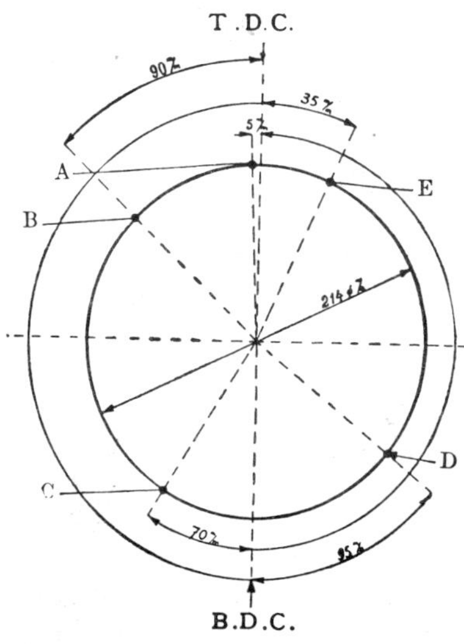

Fig. 538.—Timing Diagram. 1½-litre Model 40, Four-Cylinder.

A, Inlet opens.
B, Maximum ignition advance.
C, Inlet closes.
D, Exhaust opens.
E, Exhaust closes.

Tappet clearances—
Inlet ·35 mm. = ·013 in.
Exhaust ·45 mm. = ·017 in.
Order of firing of cylinders, 1, 2, 4, 3.

play it is necessary to lift off the caps screwed on the camshaft casing. Through the hole introduce a gauge between the rocker and the cam when it is horizontal or at the top, as shown in Fig. 535. One can then ascertain the play, calculating tenth by tenth by means of the multiple gauge, then go on to the next, and adjust one by one until the last. Having found out the play of all valves one by one, it is easy to adjust it by means of the caps. It is necessary always to

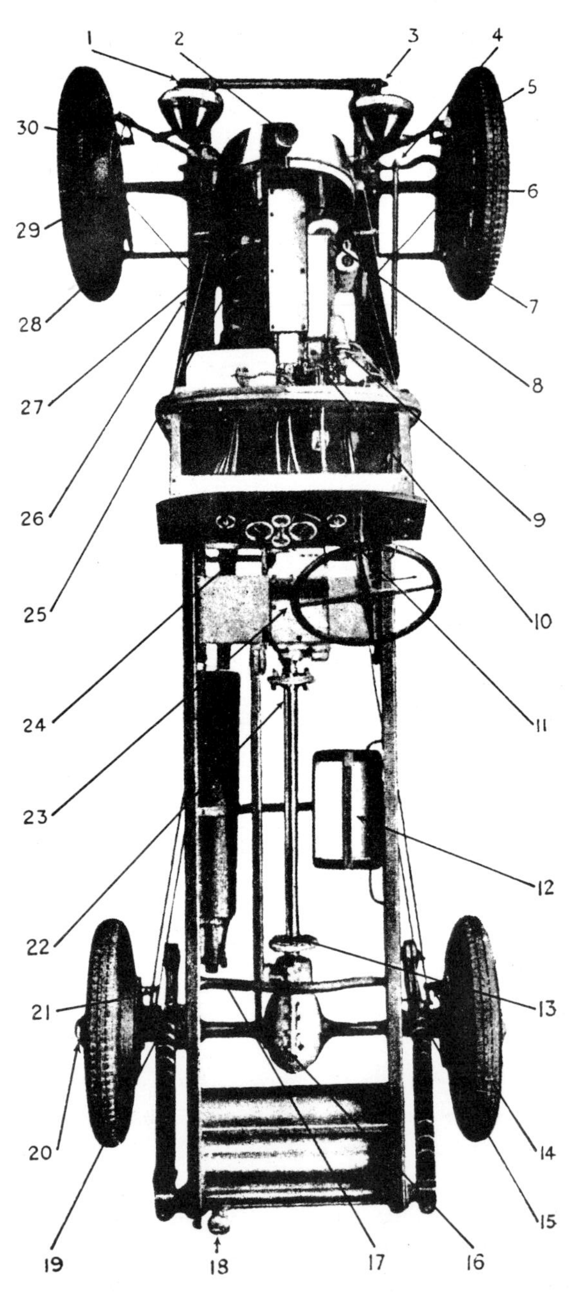

FIG. 539.—Lubrication Chart. $1\frac{1}{2}$-litre Bugatti, Model 40. The figures represent the various lubrication points.

raise the casing to adjust or change the caps and remount it to verify the play. Often it is necessary to dismount and remount it several times for one adjustment. If one has taken care to place the fly-wheel at top dead centre, the casing comes out quite easily. Care must be taken that

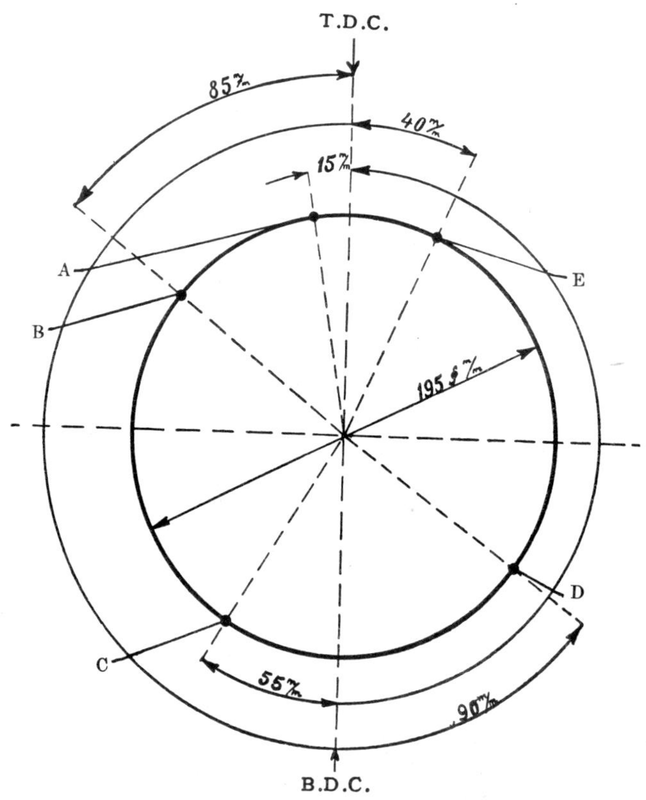

Fig. 540.—Timing Diagram. 2-litre Model 38, Eight-Cylinder.

A, Inlet opens.
B, Maximum ignition advance.
C, Inlet closes.
D, Exhaust opens.
E, Exhaust closes.

Tappet clearance for inlet and exhaust, ·5 mm. = ·019 in.
Order of firing of cylinders, 1, 5, 2, 6, 3, 7, 4, 8.

the lower part of the casing does not receive any knocks, as it has to be tight for the water circulation.

If the caps or thimbles are too short, another method is to insert steel discs or shims of the necessary thickness to take up the wear in the adjustments of the valves.

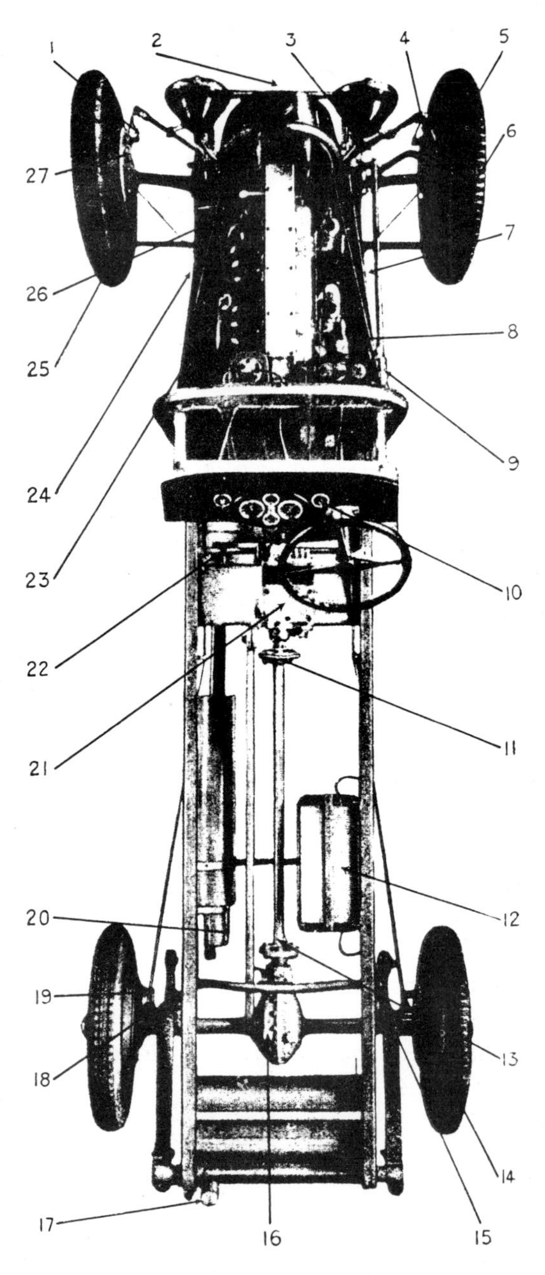

FIG. 541.—Lubrication Chart. 2-litre Bugatti, Model 38. The figures represent the various lubrication points.

For adjustment, insert a steel gauge ·05 in. between the cam and the rocker. Then turn the engine over until the cam lightly grips the gauge, sufficiently to prevent the gauge from being withdrawn. This point corresponds to the amount of opening adjustment shown in the diagram for the valve in question. Continuing to turn the engine over in the direction of running, the valve raises and recloses under the action of the cam. Then comes the moment when the cam commences to release the gauge ; when the pressure is released sufficiently to permit of sliding it, then is the moment of closing to be measured on the fly-wheel. Proceed in the same manner for each valve.

The adjusting indications are shown in millimetres on the periphery of the fly-wheel, which is 214 mm. diameter.

Engines, type 37, Nos. 1 to 155, 160, 161 to 162, and 164 are fitted with camshaft (Fig. 537).

Nos. 1 to 193 engines, type 40, also follow the indications shown in Fig. 537.

On the other hand, engines of type 37, Nos. 156 to 159, also 163 and 165 onwards, having camshafts, are adjusted in accordance with Fig. 538, as also are engines of type 40, Nos. 194 and onwards.

On the fly-wheel are to be found marked Nos. 1 and 4, which marks indicate the top dead centres of cylinders 1 and 4. On the opposite edge of the fly-wheel are the top dead centres of cylinders 2 and 3.

The order of firing is 1, 2, 4, 3, for the four-cylinder models.

The adjustment indications for the eight-cylinder models are measured on the periphery of the fly-wheel, which is 195 mm. diameter, and the order of firing in this instance is 1, 5, 2, 6, 3, 7, 4, 8.

Engine Timing

Type 40 (*Four-Cylinder*)

Valve clearance, inlet	·40 mm	
,, ,, exhaust	·50 ,,	
Inlet valve opens	6 ,,	before T.D.C
Ignition fully advanced	80 ,,	,, ,,

Type 38 (*Eight-Cylinder*)

Valve clearance, inlet	·50 mm.	
,, ,, exhaust	·50 ,,	
Inlet valve opens	15 ,,	before T.D.C.
Ignition fully advanced	85 ,,	,, ,,

Type 43 (*Grand Sports*, 2,300 *c.c.*)

Valve clearance, inlet	·50 mm.	
,, ,, exhaust	·50 ,,	
Inlet valve opens	16 ,,	before T.D.C.
Ignition fully advanced	85 ,,	,, ,,

Type 44 (*Eight-Cylinder*)

Valve clearance, inlet	·40 mm.	
,, ,, exhaust	·40 ,,	
Inlet valve opens	18 ,,	before T.D.C.
Ignition fully advanced	85 ,,	,, ,,

Type 37 (*Four-Cylinder*)

Valve clearance, inlet	·80 mm.	
,, ,, exhaust	·80 ,,	
Inlet valve opens	20 ,,	before T.D.C.
Ignition fully advanced	85 ,,	,, ,,

Types 35 *and* 35A (*Eight-Cylinder*)

Valve clearance, inlet	·50 mm.	
,, ,, exhaust	·50 ,,	
Inlet valve opens	16 ,,	before T.D.C.
Ignition fully advanced	85 ,,	,, ,,

In the case of these Bugatti cars the point of opening of the inlet valve (in mm.) for No. 1 cylinder is clearly marked on the fly-wheel, and when this is correctly set the remaining valves and cylinders automatically time themselves.

FRAZER NASH

FOUR CYLINDER

AMONG the light cars that have been used for ordinary touring as well as for competitions and racing is the Frazer Nash, having a four-cylinder engine, 69 mm. bore and 100 mm. stroke, giving a total capacity of 1,496 c.c. and an R.A.C. rating of 11·9 H.P.

The engine has its cylinders cast monobloc with the usual detachable head, and the valves are all on one side of the cylinder block, aluminium alloy pistons fitted with hollow gudgeon pins, floating type, hardened and ground with brass end caps

Lubrication is by gear pump working in the bottom of the sump driven by skew gear from the half-time shaft supplying oil to all parts of the engine under pressure. The aluminium crank-case holds about 1 gal. of oil, and the engine is suspended in the frame at three points.

The electric starter is mounted horizontally on the off-side of the rear engine bearer, while the dynamo is mounted vertically at the front of the engine, and driven by skew gear. A B.T.H. or B.L.I.C. magneto driven through the usual Simms-Vernier coupling provides the ignition. A Solex carburettor is fitted on the touring model, but the Super-Sports type of Frazer Nash has a larger carburettor (35 mm.), the cylinder head gives a higher compression ratio, the gas ports are enlarged in the cylinder block to give freer passage, the camshaft is given a slightly increased overlap, and the valve springs are aerotype, giving increased tension.

Besides the Super-Sports 11·9 H.P. Frazer Nash there is a model styled the Boulogne, which although similar in external appearance to the Super-Sports engine has several special features of its own. The cylinder head is of special design to allow high compression to be used without liability to detonation, and greater finish and balancing is given to all the reciprocating parts, the connecting rods being specially heat treated in order to reduce weight.

The general features of all these models are the same in that the clutch is a dry three plate one, Ferodo lined, the drive from the clutch is taken by a tubular clutch shaft through a hardy joint to the bevels in the back axle, a dog clutch type of sliding gear-box, to make gear changing easy, having three forward speeds, and fitted with an interlocking gear, which obviates the risk of a double gear engagement.

The standard touring car gear ratios are top 3·8 to 1,

FIG. 936.—$1\frac{1}{2}$-Litre Frazer Nash "Fast Tourer."

second speed 5·8 to 1, first speed 11·6 to 1, reverse 12 to 1. The standard wheel base is 8 ft. 9 in., track 3 ft. 10 in., and ground clearance $7\frac{1}{2}$ in., though the short chassis has a wheel base of 8 ft. 3 in. and a ground clearance of $6\frac{1}{2}$ in., while the Boulogne model has a ground clearance of 7 in. The front springs are quarter elliptic with the cornering torque taken by radius rods. The front spring has a safety leaf above the main leaf, the forward end of the safety leaf being brought well round the shackle pin. The back springs are long semi-cantilever, and both front and rear axles are fitted with Hartford shock absorbers. Rudge-Whitworth triple-spoke detachable wire wheels are fitted, and well-based Dunlop tyres, 27×4 in., are also fitted.

A C.A.V. lighting set, dynamo and battery are fitted, a Smith's rear-driven speedometer, and Tecalemit grease gun lubrication all round for the chassis.

There are very little special instructions to be given in regard to overhauling these cars, but when the clutch has done a considerable mileage, the pedal goes back further, and sometimes it is necessary to cut away or pack up the sloping floor board to prevent it pressing on the pedal all the time.

The reaction thrust when the clutch pedal is depressed is taken through a cup and ball joint situated in the middle of the hardy universal joint at the front end of the bevel casing. Although in theory there is no movement in this cup and ball, in practice a squeak is liable to develop. It is a loud squeak, and it is rather difficult to locate unless the mechanic knows about it. A drop of oil on the cup and ball will cure this.

There are also three or four points on Frazer Nash cars that require rather more frequent lubrication than the rest of the chassis, namely :—

(*a*) Reverse idler.

(*b*) The ball joints where the rear axle radius rods are attached to the frame.

(*c*) The front stub axle pivot-pins.

(*d*) The clutch ball races.

Four wheel brakes are fitted, the pedal controlling the front and rear wheels, and the hand lever that on the rear wheels only, all brakes being easily adjustable. The universal joint bearings, which operate the front wheel brakes, do not require very frequent lubrication, but they are apt to be neglected because it is necessary to lift back the dust cover and to put a little grease or oil into the joint. No greaser is provided at these points, as owners are liable to put in too much grease, and the excess of grease would be liable to work into the brake drums and spoil their action. Equally, if the car rides harshly, it is probably due to grease being required on the rear spring pad where the spring slides on the rear axle, which is apt to be forgotten when lubricating.

Beyond these points the general lubrication points of the chassis are self-evident and do not need detailed description.

TIMING AND CARBURETTOR SETTING

Fast Tourer

Valve Timing Table

Inlet opens	3° before T.D.C.
Inlet closes	50° after B.D.C.
Exhaust opens	60° before B.D.C.
Exhaust closes	16° after T.D.C.
Maximum ignition advance . .	37°-40°

Carburettor Setting (Solex)

Choke	22
Main jet	110-115 (B type)
Pilot jet	47·5

Super-Sports

Valve Timing Table

Inlet opens	3° before T.D.C.
Inlet closes	50° after B.D.C.
Exhaust opens	60° before B.D.C.
Exhaust closes	16° after T.D.C.
Maximum ignition advance . .	37°

Carburettor Setting (Solex)

Choke	25
Main jet	135 (B type)
Pilot jet	50 or 52·5

Boulogne

Valve Timing Table

Inlet opens	10° before T.D.C.
Inlet closes	65° after B.D.C.
Exhaust opens	65° before B.D.C.
Exhaust closes	35° after T.D.C.
Maximum ignition advance . .	18° (with " screened " head)

Carburettor Setting (Solex)

Choke	25 or 26
Main jet	135
Pilot jet	52·5-55

HISPANO-SUIZA

SIX CYLINDER

The six-cylinder Hispano-Suiza, rated at 37·2 H.P., has its six cylinders cast monobloc, with a bore of 100 mm. and a stroke of 140 mm. Its design is based on the aircraft engines made by this firm, so it has particularly distinctive features. The cylinders are steel forgings threaded outwardly and screwed in an aluminium chamber or cooling jacket, which is made corrosion-proof by a special process of enamelling under pressure.

This water-circulating chamber, or jacket, is fitted on each side with a large inspection plate which can be removed, so making it very easy for a thorough cleansing and removal of any deposits within it. Also, when these plates are removed, easy access is given to the nuts by means of which it is fitted on the crank-case.

The valves are overhead, fitted in a row on the cylinder head, and driven directly from a single camshaft. They are pulled back to their seats by two concentric springs, one of which is adequate to do the work should the other break.

For the purpose of adjustment of a limited amount of play between the valve disc and the rotary cam steps, a special key is provided which enables the adjustment to be made easily and in an extremely accurate manner by screwing or unscrewing the valve disc, and so altering the length of the complete valve in order to get the correct amount of clearance. The correct clearance is 2 mm., and this clearance should be made when the engine is hot, and tested with the gauge.

The makers claim that this system of valve gears, by which the cams act on the valve discs tangentially, makes for an absolutely silent-running engine.

The crankshaft is supported by seven gun-metal bearings lined with white metal. It is bored from end to end, and the lubrication ducts drilled in the crank-webs ensure a constant

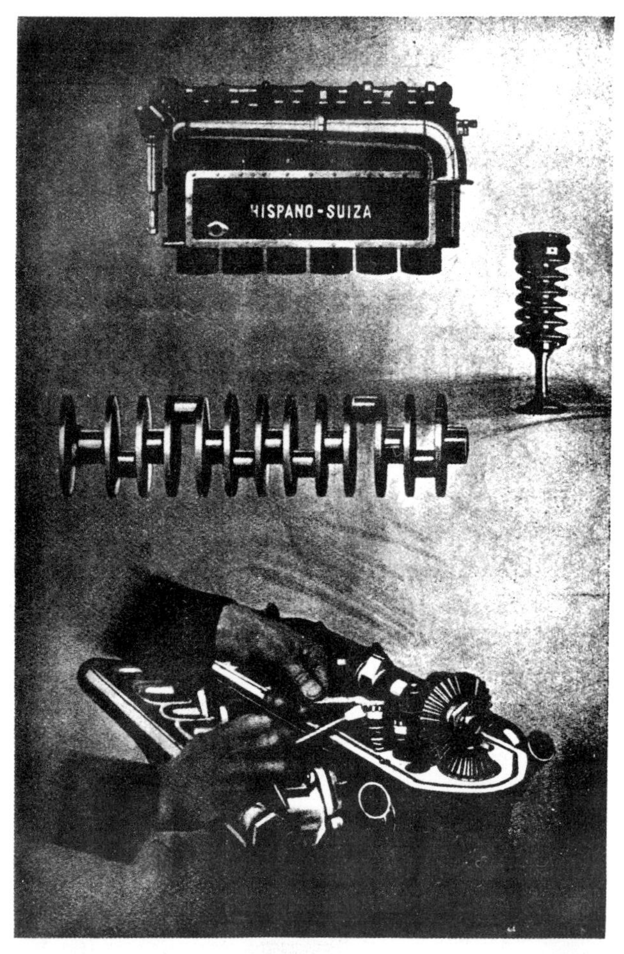

Fig. 1004.—Adjusting Valves, showing steel cylinders removed from crankcase, valve with the screw disc on its stem, the crankshaft and method of adjusting the valves.

supply of oil to the crankpins. The fly-wheel is bolted on the rearmost disc, shown on the left of the illustration, Fig. 1004, of the crankshaft.

The lubrication of the engine is effected by a pump with

rotary valves fitted at the bottom of the crank-case, which constitutes an oil well. A cover is fitted over the valve gear, which has to be removed if any attention is needed to the lubrication system of the valves. Their supply of oil is made by a special branch duct leading to the rearmost bearing of the camshaft. The oil is then forced into this shaft in which the duct is drilled, and through which a flow of lubricant will thus be made to pass. The supply is further distributed to the various cams and bearings by a number of small holes drilled in the shaft. Each valve disc is provided, moreover, with a small hole for the lubrication of the valve stem in its guide.

The excess oil supply forced into the camshaft flows out of the foremost end of the shaft and drips on the valve gear drive pinion on its way back to the crank-case well. A safety valve limits the oil pressure, which is indicated by a pressure gauge fitted on the dashboard. A level-indicating device with a float shows also the quantity of oil in the crank-case or sump.

The Solex carburettor is of the double type with automatic sprays fitted with one constant level chamber, each of the carburetting elements feeding independently a set of three cylinders. The volumes of gas to be admitted are adjusted by a double rotary slide valve. In addition, two levers are provided for the purpose of adjustment of the mixture, one in slow-running condition and the other in the normal running condition. The normal setting is 2 main jets 160, 2 pilot jets 75.

The main petrol tank holds 24 gals. and supplies the autovac fitted on the dashboard.

The centrifugal pump has a capacity of circulating about 12 gals. of water at a speed of 1,200 revs. per min. The total capacity of the water-circulating system is about 7 gals.

Two batteries of accumulators are charged by a dynamo of the bi-compound wound type rated for a supply of 18 amps. at 12 volts under full running conditions. This dynamo begins to generate current as soon as the speed of the engine reaches 400 revs. per min. A compensated regulator is provided in the circuit which acts as a charging current limiter to prevent the battery being overcharged. Each battery has a capacity of 75 amp. hours.

Dual ignition is fitted, each having its own set of plugs, with the current distributors of the Delco type. A centrifugal governor automatically controls the advance and retarding of the ignition, which the driver can increase as regards his own requirements by means of the control mounted on the steering wheel. With the ignition lever fully retarded, the points should break at 85 mm. after T.D.C.

The wiring diagram shows the lay-out of the electrical system, the cables of which are of the monofil type or one pole system, the return current being earthed. Each cable end is fitted with an ebonite ring bearing a reference number for fitting up purposes. The distribution box placed on the left below the footboard is provided for the connection of accessory electrical apparatus, such as Klaxon horns, ceiling lamps, cigar lighters, etc. Further, two terminals are provided to permit connecting the cables for the recharge of the batteries at the garage without removing them from the car should that necessity arise. These terminals will be found behind the instrument board immediately below the switch-board.

Brake Adjustment.—It is necessary that all four wheels should be raised for adjusting the brakes.

For adjustment of the foot brake (1) adjust the servo brake. To do this loosen the safety nut and tighten the adjustment screw until on depressing the foot lever the latter remains jammed in the position in which it is placed when you cease depressing it ; then loosen the adjustment screw until the foot lever comes back by itself to its position of rest, and until the drum can be rotated freely by hand from the rear towards the front ; bring back the pedal as far as possible towards the foot of the driver ; (2) adjust the tension of the forward control cables until, when the wheels are deviated first one way and then the other, one feels on rotating the wheels by hand that the deviation is followed immediately by contact of the brake cheeks with the drum on the inner face of the wheel ; (3) then some one must get into the driver's seat and depress the brake pedal gently ;

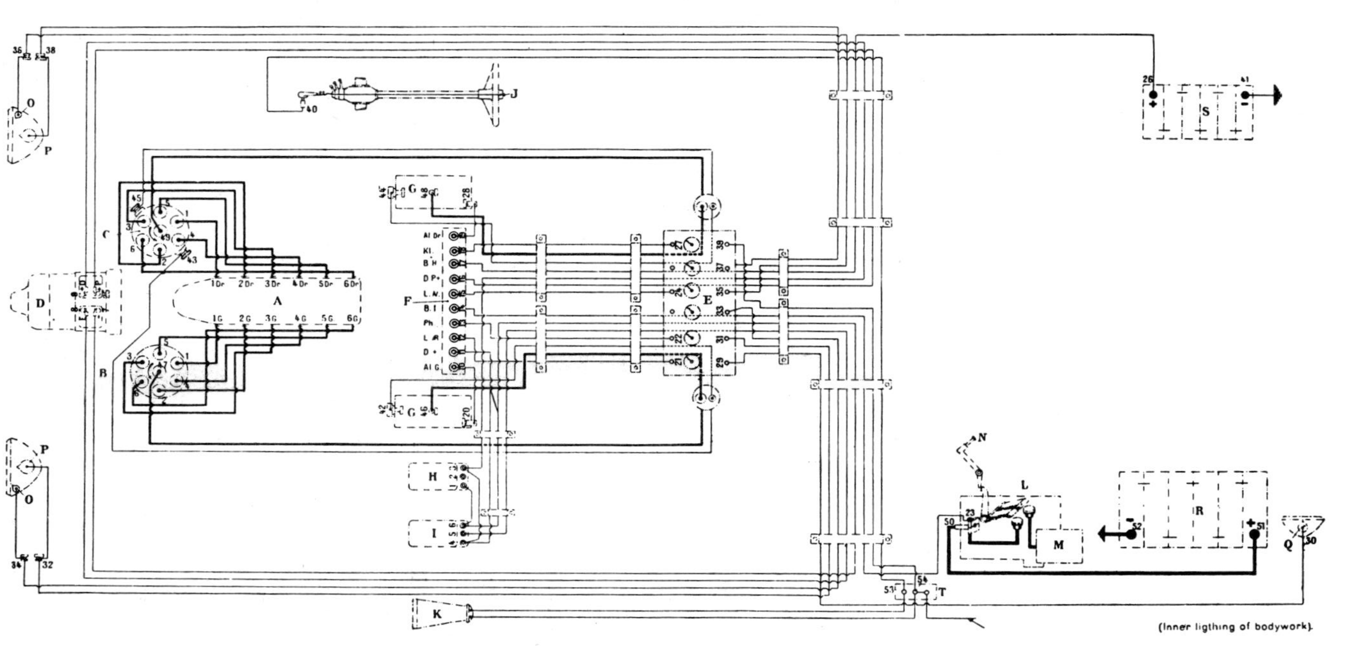

FIG. 1005.—Electrical Wiring Diagram.

then adjust the tension of the rear control cables until the braking action on the rear wheel is equal to that on the front wheel.

Should the brake act more quickly on one of the four wheels than on the other, regulate this by means of the clips placed behind each of the brake brackets.

The best working of the rocking lever by the control levers is obtained if the latter are slightly out of, and in front of the vertical position at the moment when they exert their effort. If it should be found after a certain number of attempts at adjustments that the levers leave this position, they should be brought back to it by means of the screw with a top fitted for this purpose on the small compensation differential, after having slackened the tension nuts of the cables.

If it is necessary to dismantle the disc which carries the jaws of the servo brake, unscrew the adjustment nut of the brake cables on the right-hand side; dismantle the right-hand half of the brake rocking lever; remove the two bolts of the bracket and withdraw the axle from its square holder; dismantle the square sleeve (taper pin) and the control connecting the disc with the pedal, then pull the disc out.

For refitting, carry out the same operations in the reverse order.

If necessary to dismantle the front brake drum, take the wheel off and dismantle the brake barrel of the wheel. To do this the barrel is driven towards the inside of the hub, and the annular brake, which holds it, is removed with a screw-driver; remove the pin of the swivel nut and unscrew this nut, which has a left-handed thread on the left side.

In adjusting the hand brake the rear wheels must be jammed or locked when the pawl of the hand brake catches in the fifth notch of the brake lever sector. When the brake is released, the control cable must not touch the pulley of the servo brake. To dismantle the rear brake drum take the wheel off and remove the pins of all the nuts of the studs by which the drum is fastened to the hub, and unscrew these nuts ; pull the hub out—it will come out with the differential shaft ; remove the pin of the nut by means of which the ball race is locked on the rear axle tube, then unscrew this nut ; this is a left-handed thread on the left or near-side wheel ; pull out the ball bearing and then the drum.

If a chattering noise is produced in the rear on account of lateral play of the rear axle spring pads, the following things should be done to remedy it : (1) dismantle the adjusting nut locking device after having removed the screw ; (2) tighten home the adjusting nut on the spring plates, then unscrew one notch to allow the pad the necessary freedom of oscillation ; (3) replace the adjustment nut locking device.

With regard to the front axle, note the wooden or fibre wedges placed underneath the springs ; if they are of tapering shape they will have to be replaced with their big ends turned towards the front if at any time this axle is taken down or the springs demounted.

Gear-Box and Clutch.—If it is required to dismantle the gear-box and the cone clutch, the method of procedure is as follows : (1) dismantle the self-starter and disconnect this from the main battery at the battery taper terminal, taking care to attach the wire at a good distance from the terminal in order to prevent short circuit ; remove the wires by means of which the starter is supplied with current ; remove the four nuts of the studs by means of which the starter is secured to the casing and pull the starter out ; (2) dismantle the brake rocking lever ; remove the two bolts from each of the brackets and pull the axles out of their square holders ; remove the cover of the gear-box (nine nuts have to be unscrewed) ; remove the clutch pedal gear (two bolts securing the lever bracket) ; disconnect the hand brake, servo brake, and clutch controls ; (3) dismantle the front cardan shaft ; take the fastening screws out of the covering ring ; take out the upper part of the servo brake casing (eight bolts) ; withdraw the pin from the ball joint, after which remove the spring ; withdraw the four fastening screws of the retaining ring screw of the trunnion block ; drive the retaining screw backwards ; take out the ball joint with its trunnion blocks ;

(4) remove the nuts by means of which the gear-case is secured to the engine (fourteen bolts and two studs), then pull out the gear-box case; withdraw the six nuts with pins from the studs by means of which the clutch crown is secured to the fly-wheel; remove the crown and the clutch.

In order to fit up again, carry out the same operations inversely, whilst taking the following precautions: carefully lubricate the thrust ball bearing fitted in the end of the crankshaft, and the purpose of which is to centre the coupling shaft; lubricate the coupling hub in order to facilitate its sliding. Carefully replace the coupling on the shaft wing and the coupling crown on the fly-wheel in accordance with the reference points marked upon them.

In order to dismantle the disc coupling after having taken out the gear-box, as stated above, dismantle the self-starter tooth crown, which is fastened by twelve nuts, after which the coupling will come off.

In order to withdraw the twenty-four clutch pressure springs fit on the three special spring pressure screws (three holes are provided for this purpose) and drive their nuts against the disc; remove the six screws by means of which the adjustment disc is fastened and dismantle the disc by means of the special spanner by screwing on; loosen the nuts of the pressure screws progressively, then withdraw the springs.

In order to refit again, the same operations have to be carried out in the reverse order, while carefully lubricating the slide of the discs on its wings, and replace the starter tooth crown on the fly-wheel with its reference points coinciding.

In order to adjust the displacement of the clutch, compress the springs by means of the three tension screws, and unscrew the six screws of the adjustment disc, carrying out the adjustment by means of the special spanner. Holes are made in the disc to provide a working space for the spanner. When the adjustment has been carried out, see that the nuts are locked again.

Rear Axle.—To dismantle the rear axle (1) disconnect the

intermediate cardan shaft; this is necessary, otherwise it will be too difficult to replace the rear ball joint trunnion; dismantle the front cardan shaft and remove the screws by means of which the covering ring is fastened; withdraw the upper part of the servo brake casing (eight bolts); withdraw the pins from the ball joint head after having removed the spring; withdraw the four screws by means of which the hand screw of the ball joint trunnions are fastened; drive the band backwards; dismantle the dust shield bracket of the thrust ball casing (eight nuts) and the flexible tube of the ball joint lubrication (one joint); pull out the cardan shaft; (2) hoist the chassis by a pulley block, or jack it up high enough to allow the rear axle to pass under the petrol tank; dismantle the wheels, also the casing shields of the ball races of the thrust bearing (four nuts), the spindles of the brake cable fork, and the four pins of the spring shackles. Take the rear axle out. When fitting up again, the same operation should be repeated in the reverse order.

Steering Gear.—To dismantle the steering gear disconnect (1) at the bottom the Klaxon horn terminal, the two control levers of the carburettor adjustment gear, and the advance ignition control lever; remove the locking nut of the sector support, the accelerator support and its fastening plate (two bolts); remove the dust shield of the steering lever (four bolts) and the four bolts used for fastening the steering gear; withdraw the steering lever either from its upper holder if the chassis is fitted with a body, or from the ball joint casing of the controlling rod of the steering gear; (2) at the upper part, unscrew the sector, turn it round and take it off with the controls; dismantle the steering wheel (one bolt); withdraw the control sector of the throttle (one bolt) and then the tube; pull the steering gear out downwards. When fitting up, the same operation should be repeated in the reverse order, taking care as regards the steering lever to place the wheels in a straight line, parallel, and place the lever in a vertical position at half a turn of the steering wheel.

Cylinder Head.—If it is required to dismantle the cylinder block, disconnect the circulation water piping, the exhaust manifold, the inlet manifold, the drive of the revolution counter, the piping of the oil pressure gauge, the oil feed pipe to the cylinder block, the petrol feed pipe to the carburettor, the petrol supply pipe, the two levers of the carburettor adjustment controls (this should be done at the ball joints to prevent putting the adjustment out of order), the accelerator drive (at the ball joints), the accelerator pull-off spring, the two cylinder closing plates; remove all the pins from the nuts by means of which the cylinder block is fitted on the casing; remove the rear clamps by means of which the heads of the Delco distributors are fastened. The cylinder block can then be taken off by means of a pulley block.

To dismantle the valve spring it is necessary to dismantle the drive of the revolution counter, take off the camshaft cover, the caps of the camshaft bearings, and dismantle the camshaft. After having placed the corresponding piston at its T.D.C. in order to prevent the valve falling inside the cylinder, compress the springs with the valve dismantling tool, unscrew the valve head, and then replace the spring or springs as necessary. When refitting, the same operations have to be performed in the reverse order.

To prevent upsetting the timing of the camshaft, place it in such a manner that the admission or inlet cam of the six cylinder is in the valve driving position and that the ignition distributor is on contact No. 1, the crankshaft being at the T.D.C. position of Nos. 1 and 6 cylinders. The nuts of the camshaft bearing studs must only be moderately tightened.

The valve timing for Hispano-Suiza engines is as follows:—

Inlet opens	35 mm. after T.D.C.
Inlet closes	180 mm. after B.D.C.
Exhaust opens . . .	150 mm. before B.D.C.
Exhaust closes . . .	35 mm. after T.D.C.

The measurements given are to be taken from the periphery of the fly-wheel.

The Engine.—If it is necessary to take the complete

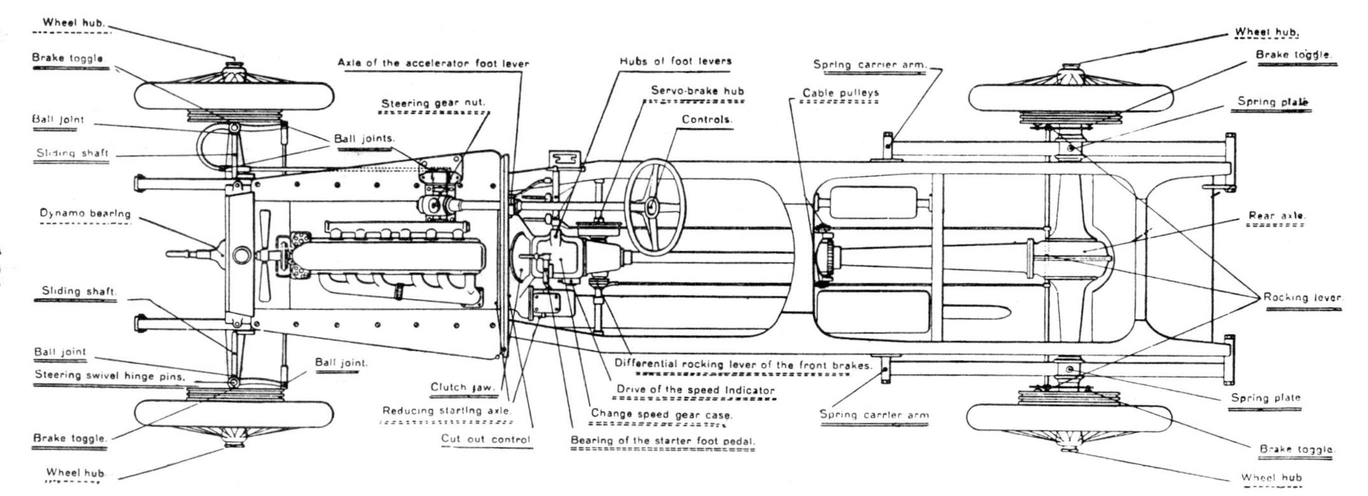

Fig. 1006.—Lubrication Diagram.

engine out of the chassis, the best method to be followed is to dismantle the following details in the undermentioned order :—

1. The radiator.
2. The dynamo.
3. The fan and its belt.
4. The inlet piping.
5. The exhaust header.
6. The exhaust pipe, by unscrewing it at the free escape bend.
7. The bonnet rest boards.
8. The steering gear.
9. The flexible cable of the revolution counter.
10. The oil pressure gauge pipe.
11. The pipe supplying oil to the cylinder head.
12. The petrol feed pipe.
13. The electrical wire guide tubes.
14. The gear-box.
15. The eight bolts by means of which the engine is fastened to the chassis.
16. The seven bolts by means of which the engine is fitted to the dashboard.
17. The four clamps below the engine lugs.

The engine can then be removed from the chassis by means of a pulley block and slings.

INVICTA

SIX CYLINDER

There are two Invicta models, both having six-cylinder overhead valved engines with the usual detachable head. The smaller is rated at 19·5 H.P., and its cylinders have a bore of 72·5 mm. with a stroke of 120 mm., giving a total cubic capacity of 2,972 c.c., and is usually known as the 3-litre model Invicta.

The other model is usually styled the 4½-litre with its cylinders of 88·5 mm. bore and 120 mm. stroke, having a total cubic capacity of 4,134 c.c.

As the 3-litre was so successful and satisfactory in general design, the manufacturers produced the 4½-litre six-cylinder engine identical in general principles with that of the 3-litre, but the front axle, back axle, gear-box, and propeller shaft have been increased in size and strength in the latter model by 100 per cent., while the size of the brakes is increased to 14 in., otherwise the general design and lay-out is the same as the 3-litre. It is rated at 29·1 H.P. The tappet clearances of these models is inlet ·003 in. and exhaust ·004 in., adjusted when the engine is warm. The order of firing of the cylinders is 1, 4, 2, 6, 3, 5. The valve timing is set as follows :—

Inlet opens .	10° before T.D.C.	Exhaust opens .	60° before B.D.C.
Inlet closes .	50° after B.D.C.	Exhaust closes .	15° after T.D.C.

Hand advance is provided only for the ignition of 25°, and the contact points gap is ·012 in.

Rotax coil ignition is usually found fitted on Invicta cars though sometimes Simms S.R. 6 magneto is found fitted on the 4½-litre, so it has dual ignition, and the cylinder head is so modified as to allow of two sets of sparking plugs being fitted. In chassis built previous to the autumn of 1927 magneto ignition only was fitted.

On the 3-litre Invicta each group of three cylinders has

its own carburettor and inlet pipes, so that any moment each carburettor is only supplying mixture to one cylinder at a time, and as it is very difficult to synchronise each of two

Fig. 1028.—3-litre Engine with Dual Carburettor and small balance pipe in between them.

carburettors exactly, a small balance pipe is provided which keeps the two inlet pipes in communication. Two makes of carburettors are supplied with Invicta 3-litre car as standard alternatives, the Solex and the S.U. On the 4½-litre model two S.U. carburettors are fitted, with a special adjustment at the base of carburettor whereby the position of the special needle jets can be varied.

The 3-litre has a petrol tank carried in the rear, holding 12 gals., to supply the autovac tank on the dashboard. That of the 4½-litre model is 14, including 2 gals. in reserve.

The 4½-litre crank-case takes 1¾ gals. of oil, and the radiator 4 gals. of water.

The foot brakes are adjusted by screwing the wing-nuts attached to the end of each brake rod. In order to prevent confusion between foot and hand brake on the rear axle, the hand brake adjustments are wheel-shaped and the foot brake adjustments are wing-nuts.

It should always be possible to lock the rear wheels with the hand brake when properly adjusted.

A Bendix pinion is meshed with the fly-wheel gear for starting up the engine, and if it gets jammed at any time, it usually can be cleared by rocking the car in gear by hand. To see if it is jammed, remove the Bendix inspection plug in the fly-wheel casing near the engine starter and see whether the pinion appears meshed with the fly-wheel. Try whether it can be prised out of mesh with the screw-driver. If by rocking or with the screw-driver the Bendix pinion cannot be disengaged, slacken the self-starter holding down bolts, and prise the pinion out of mesh to the rear. Special Marles steering is used on Invicta cars, and the adjustment is no different from that of other cars fitted with this type of steering already described, such as the A.C.

The usual oil pressure shown on the gauge when the 4½-litre is warm running at a road speed of 20 miles an hour is 15 lbs. per square inch, while when the engine is idling 10 lbs. should be shown on the gauge. There are four rings on the pistons, and the piston clearances are ·004 in. The 12-volt Rotax lighting set has a battery of 85 amp. hours, and the dynamo charging rate is under normal conditions 10 amp. at a road speed of 20 miles an hour on top gear. The clutch pedal clearance is ½ in. from the board, and there is no clutch adjustment.

MERCÉDÈS

SIX AND EIGHT CYLINDERS

MERCÉDÈS have joined with the Benz Company since 1927, so that now their full title is Mercédès-Benz, though the cars themselves, known as Mercédès, are manufactured by the Daimler-Benz A.G. at Stuttgart-Untertürkheim, Germany. As far as the British market is concerned, it is the supercharged models which have received support and are found running in this country. These are the six-cylinder 24 H.P. with 80 × 130 mm. bore and stroke and overhead valved supercharged engine, the six-cylinder 33 H.P. with 94 × 150 mm. supercharged overhead valved engine, and six-cylinder 36 H.P. 98 × 150 mm. supercharged overhead valved engine, as well as the six-cylinder 16 H.P. 65 × 100 mm., and the eight-cylinder 32 H.P. 80 × 115 mm. side valved and not supercharged power units. As, however, the servicing of one applies to all, the six-cylinder supercharged models are taken here as an example of Mercédès modern practice.

The six cylinders are a single aluminium casting with inserted grey cast-iron liners. The 6-litre motor has the 94 mm. bore and 150 mm. stroke, and the 4-litre engine 80 mm. bore and 130 mm. stroke. The firing order, counting No. 1 cylinder nearest radiator, is 1, 5, 3, 6, 2, 4. These cylinders and their water-cooling jackets are cast in one with the upper half of the crank-case. On top of this casting is fitted the detachable cylinder head, with which is fitted the usual copper asbestos gasket. The valves are of the overhead vertical type with one inlet and one exhaust per cylinder, with mushroom heads on conical seatings.

The skeleton lay-out illustration (Fig. 1157) shows the arrangement of the working parts. The rear end of the crankshaft is fitted with a worm for driving the vertical shaft, which operates the geared oil pump situated below this shaft and carried by the rearmost bearing support. Also, by means of two helical gears, the vertical shaft drives the camshaft which runs along the top of the cylinders. Further helical gearing fitted on this vertical shaft also operates the centrifugal water pump, the dynamo, and the magneto, coupled together in tandem and mounted on the exhaust side of the engine.

The Mercédès "Pallas" carburettor is shown in section in Fig. 1158, in order that its working details can be clearly seen. In connection with the main jet *c*, the jet holder c_1 can be removed after unscrewing its closing plug c_2. At the bottom end of this jet holder is fitted a calibrated fuel nozzle *c*. When the latter is obstructed it must be cleaned only by blowing out, or replaced by another jet, which must then also be screwed into the holder.

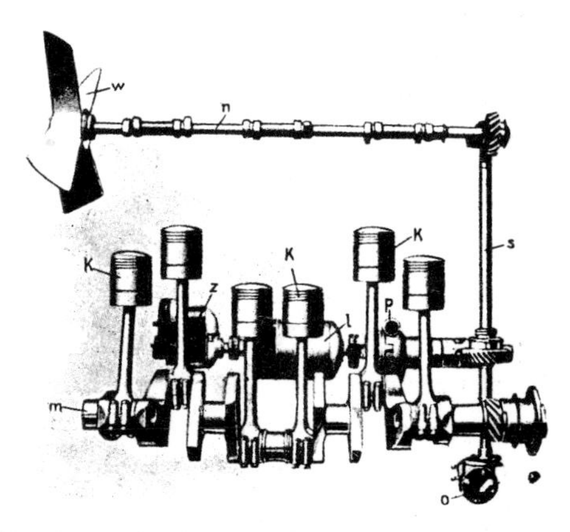

Fig. 1157.—Crankshaft and Camshaft with Vertical Drive.

k, Piston.
l, Dynamo.
m, Crankshaft.
n, Camshaft.
o, Oil pump.
p, Water circulating pump.
s, Vertical shaft for driving camshaft.
w, Fan.
z, Magneto.

When it is required to obtain access to the slow-running jet *p*, the hexagon plug p_1 (or cap) is unscrewed and the jet *p* can then be unscrewed for cleaning. It is hardly likely that the fuel-feed tube with riser *h* will have to be removed, as the bore is sufficiently wide to prevent accumulation of impurities. As supercharged engines are rather a novel proposition to the ordinary garage, the method of working of the carburettor is given in full, so that knowing the principle, should adjustments be required, the work of finding the fault is rendered easier by this knowledge.

When the engine works without the assistance of the supercharger, the two throttles *d* and *z* of the carburettor are

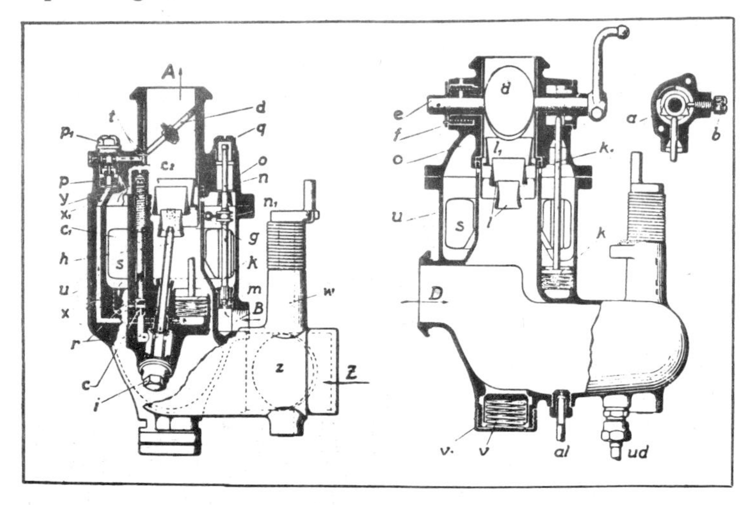

FIG. 1158.—Mercédès Carburettor in Section.

A, Union for induction pipe.
a, Stop and controlling cam.
B, Fuel-feed nipple.
b, Slow-running adjustment screw.
c, Calibrated main jet.
c_1. Calibrated main jet holder.
c_2, Slotted cap for main jet holder.
D, Compressed air induction pipe.
d, Throttle.
e, Throttle spindle.
f, Closing spring for throttle.
g, Horse-shoe shaped float counter-weight.
h, Fuel-feed pipe.
i. Hexagon cap covering feed pipe.
j, Injection plunger.
k_1, Injection plunger spindle.
l, Choke tube.
l_1, Automatic air regulator.
m, Valve seating of the float needle.
n, Float needle.
n_1, Float needle collar.
o, Upper half of carburettor body.
p, Slow-running jet.
p_1, Hexagon cap covering slow-running jet.
q, Hexagon cap covering float needle.
r, Duct between main jet and petrol feed pipe.
s, Annular float.
t, Duct for slow running.
u, Bottom half of carburettor body.
v, Safety (relief) valve.
v_1, Screwed cap closing the safety valve.
w, Spindle of air-supply throttle (*z*).
xx_1, Duct for admission of fuel to slow-running jet.
y, Duct for admission of air to slow-running jet.
Z, Normal air-inlet pipe of carburettor.
z, Air-supply throttle, closed when running with supercharger.
al, Small petrol drain pipe.
ud, Union for autovac connection.

open, and air, preheated more or less, according to the position of the hot-air damper fitted in the jacket of the exhaust muff, is drawn in at each suction stroke through the choke tubes *l*.

At the same time, fuel enters from the float chamber through the calibrated nozzle *c* into the space in which protrudes the end of the fuel tube *h*, is elevated by suction in the riser of the latter, and issues in the centre of the narrowest choke tube *l*, where it mixes with the supply of air drawn in, and is finely atomised by the additional supply of air which rises in the annular space between the inner and the outer choke tubes. The mixture of fuel and air which is produced in this manner issues through the induction nipple A and is supplied to the cylinders. In this particular carburettor the main jet is fitted in a special jet holder c_1, which is connected with the petrol-feed tube by a duct *r*, which leads from the float chamber to the petrol-feed tube. Owing to this arrangement, the fuel jet *c* can easily be replaced without loss of fuel. This replacement is effected merely by unscrewing the main jet holder c_1, which can then be removed, together with the main jet, which can be unscrewed from its holder and replaced by another.

If now the speed of the air current flowing through the carburettor is increased owing to increased working speed of the engine, the increased suction thus produced lifts the automatic air regulator l_1, which is free to slide up and down in the bore of the air-supply chamber. This displacement provides an additional annular space for the admission of the gas mixture. The proportions of the mixture of air and fuel are thus corrected in accordance with the increase of speed in such a manner that a more economical consumption of fuel is secured by means of this automatic regulation.

The throttle *d* is practically closed in slow-running conditions, so cutting out main jet *c*. The increased vacuum thus produced acts through a duct *t*, which is provided on the edge of the throttle and connects with the hexagon cap p_1, which covers the slow-running jet *p*, which is fitted below the screwed plug. This slow-running jet communicates with the space situated below the carburettor plunger *k* by means of a duct *x*, which runs first vertically and then horizontally towards the bottom part of the carburettor, and through which it receives its supply of petrol. Furthermore, the air space in the upper part of the carburettor, which communicates with the inner part of the carburettor above the float, is connected with the annular space round the slow-running jet *p* by means of three oblique ducts *y* in such a manner that the slow-running jet is supplied with air, as described above.

Fuel can be injected as required, prior to the engine being started up, by working the carburettor plunger spindle k_1, together with the carburettor or injection plunger *k*, which is fitted at the end of this spindle. This is done by turning repeatedly to and fro the throttle spindle *e* with the stop and controlling cam *a*, the accelerator pedal being moved up and down for this purpose. When this is done, the injection plunger presses fuel through duct *x*, first horizontally and then vertically, inside the wall of the bottom half of the carburettor body and through the oblique duct x_1 in the upper part of the carburettor body, which communicates with duct *x*, towards the slow-running jet *p*.

The annular float *s*, the purpose of which is to keep the fuel level constant in the carburettor into which the fuel enters through the induction nipple B, is attached to a horse-shoe shaped double lever *g*. This also plays the part of a float counterweight, with the float needle *n*, which is fitted laterally, and this lever *g* is connected by means of its free end with the collar of the float needle n_1. When the level of the liquid rises in the float chamber, the float is lifted together with the horse-shoe shaped arm of the float counter-weight *g*, whilst the other arm of the double lever sinks, pulling down the float needle *n* by means of its guide collar n_1. This needle is thus pressed down on its seating *m*, situated above the fuel admission pipe, in such a manner as to prevent the inflow of any further fuel.

Means are provided for rendering the float needle easily accessible (for the purpose, for instance, of removing any impurities which may adhere to the point, by turning the needle backwards and forwards). By removing the screwed cap *q* the upper end of the float needle is then exposed. The upper half *o* of the carburettor body and the intermediate ring must be unscrewed when it is found necessary to remove the float needle altogether, greatest care being taken, however,

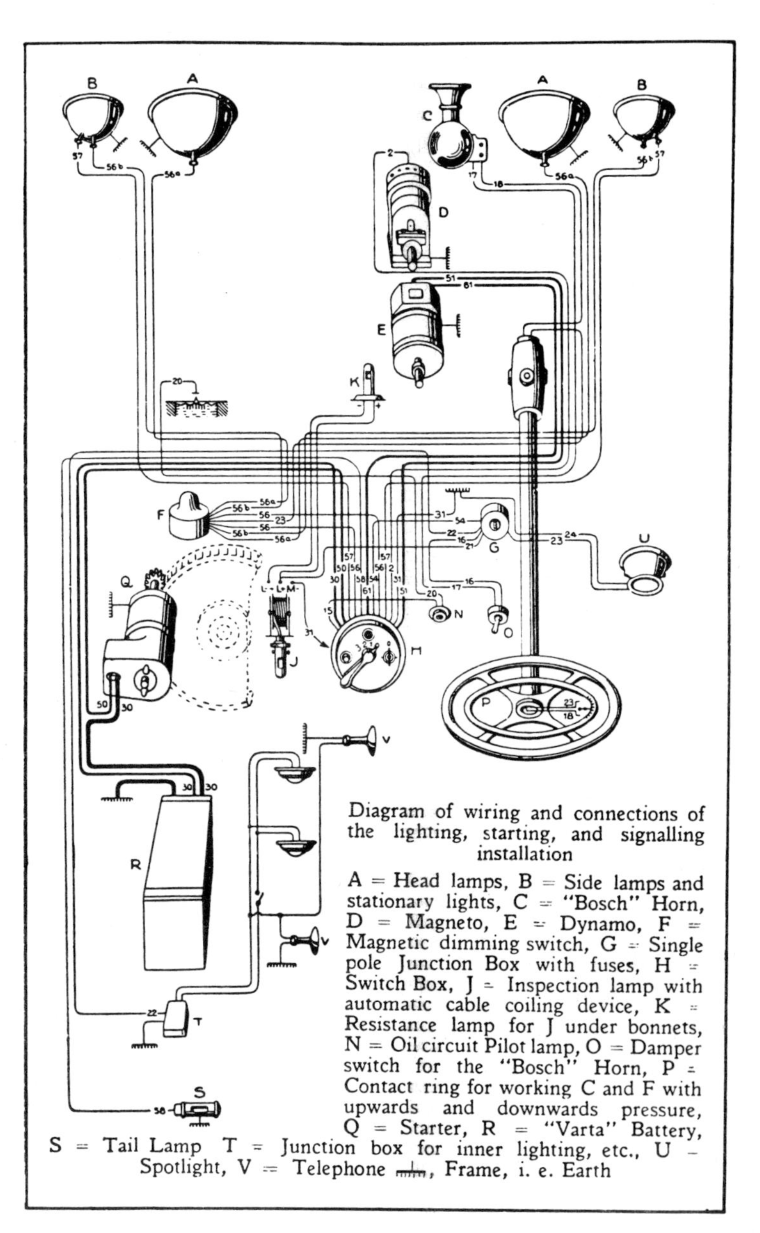

Diagram of wiring and connections of the lighting, starting, and signalling installation

A = Head lamps, B = Side lamps and stationary lights, C = "Bosch" Horn, D = Magneto, E = Dynamo, F = Magnetic dimming switch, G = Single pole Junction Box with fuses, H = Switch Box, J = Inspection lamp with automatic cable coiling device, K = Resistance lamp for J under bonnets, N = Oil circuit Pilot lamp, O = Damper switch for the "Bosch" Horn, P = Contact ring for working C and F with upwards and downwards pressure, Q = Starter, R = "Varta" Battery, S = Tail Lamp T = Junction box for inner lighting, etc., U = Spotlight, V = Telephone ⏊, Frame, i. e. Earth

Fig. 1159.—Wiring Diagram.

to make sure the paper joint is again fitted intact above and below the intermediate ring.

Any fuel which may overflow through the petrol-feed tube *h* collects in the lowest part of the carburettor, whence it is removed through a small pipe *al*.

As already explained, in these carburettors the calibrated main jet *c* is not embodied in the riser of the petrol-feed tube *h*, which protrudes into the choke tube, but is fitted on the end of a jet holder c_1, which is screwed laterally downwards into the carburettor body in such a manner that a supply of fuel from the float chambers flows towards the transversal openings of the nozzle, whilst the calibrated vertical bore of the jet communicates by means of a duct with the space into which protrudes the bottom end of the petrol-feed tube. Should it be found necessary to change the main jet, the only operation required in this design is removal of the main jet holder c_1 by unscrewing same and the replacement of the fuel jet *c* screwed into the end of this jet holder. The main jet holder c_1 is then replaced. This operation does not involve any loss of fuel and does not necessitate removal of the carburettor or unscrewing of its component parts. The only precaution which is essential is to ascertain that the slotted nut c_2 is screwed well home on the flange of the carburettor when the main jet nozzle has been replaced.

Replacement of the slow-running jet *p* is quite easily carried out also, and is effected by merely unscrewing the threaded cap p_1, when the jet *p* can be unscrewed and replaced. In this case also it is important to make sure that the threaded cap p_1 is screwed well home when the jet is inserted again, and not to forget the washer. The box spanner for the slow-running jet should be kept in a wooden case, which should contain four different main jets and two slow-running jets as spares. All these are given with new cars.

When the supercharger is operated, a branch of the pedal-rod gear which is connected with the blower clutch closes the air-supply throttle fitted in the normal air-inlet pipe z of the carburettor, by turning the vertical air-supply throttle spindle *w* whilst the clutch engages. In these circumstances, the combustion air is supplied to the carburettor under pressure through the union D situated on the left, and the atomisation of the fuel takes place in the same manner as when running without the supercharger.

Under these conditions the normal suction of the autovac tank is suspended and is replaced by a pressure which is produced by the supercharger, and is conveyed to the top

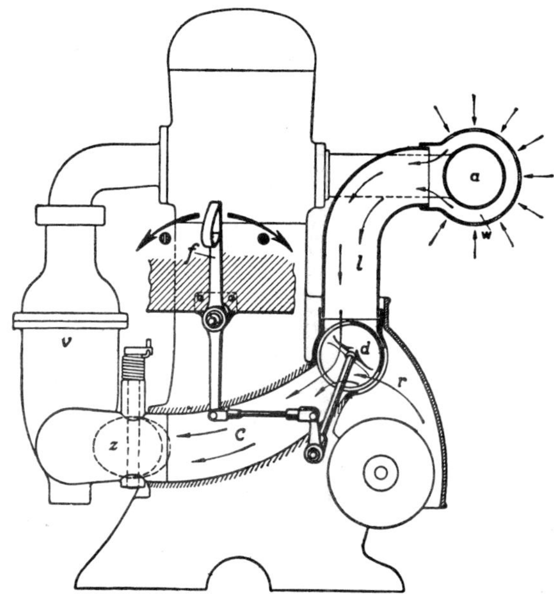

FIG. 1160.—Air-Supply Diagram for Carburettor.

a, Exhaust muff.
c, Air-supply duct.
d, Butterfly valve of air-supply throttle.
f, Foot lever.
l, Pipe connecting preheater sleeve with air-supply throttle.
r, Space in which engine auxiliaries are accommodated (magneto, etc.).
v, Carburettor.
w, Preheater sleeve.
z, Air-supply valve.

of the autovac tank through the connection *ud*, the end of which is fitted with a non-return valve. The autovac is put out of action in this manner, and the fuel which the auxiliary contains is now conveyed under pressure to the carburettor. In the event of backfiring, the bottom part of the carburettor is fitted with a relief valve *b*, designed as a spring-loaded safety valve, which opens in such cases and brings about a compensation of the pressures.

In the course of running without the supercharger, the air supply of this type of carburettor is effected, as shown diagrammatically by the accompanying sketch (Fig. 1160), through the intermediary of a duct *c*, which runs through the upper half of the crank-case. The fresh air supplied according to the position of the throttle *d*, which is fitted in the induction pipe *l*, below exhaust muff *a*, either from the upper part of the space *r* without any special preheating (this space *r* contains the three engine auxiliaries referred to above), or from the heating chamber *w*, which surrounds the exhaust pipe *a* in such a manner that the air supply of the carburettor flows first through the exhaust muff and is preheated in this manner. The displacement of the throttle *d* is controlled by working a pivoted pedal *f* mounted at the bottom of the dashboard. The butterfly of the throttle gives a full bore admission of air from the pipe *l*, when the pedal is depressed hard against the right-hand (black) stop. At the point of issue from the crank-case of the fresh air induction duct *c*, the carburettor *v* is connected with an elbow pipe, in which is inserted an air-supply throttle *z*, which remains open as long as normal working conditions of the carburettor prevail, but closes, owing to its connection with the supercharger controlling rod gear, as soon as the blower is started working.

The bottom arm of the accelerator pedal is connected to the rod gear, which connects the lever fitted on the spindle on the carburettor throttle.

The supercharger is mounted in front of the engine and constitutes with its driving gear, clutch, and brake an independent mechanical unit. It comprises a casing provided with cooling fins completely enclosed and fitted with a silencer. In this casing rotate two vertical blower vanes, one of which drives the other through the intermediary of a set of spur gears fitted on their respective shafts. This blower draws in air from the space situated below the exhaust muff in which the engine auxiliaries are accommodated, through the silencer, compresses this air and forces it from below through the carburettor. In the carburettor this compressed air is mixed with atomised fuel and thence forced into the cylinders through the induction pipe of the engine.

The blower is started by depressing completely the accelerator pedal, whereby the plate clutch fitted on the front extension of the crankshaft is engaged and a rapid rotary motion is imparted to the pair of bevel gears which drive the vanes of the blower. A brake of the same design as the driving clutch, and mounted coaxially with the latter, provides a rapid stoppage on the vanes of the supercharger on releasing the accelerator pedal. Just like an ordinary clutch stop does for changing gear.

When it is necessary to dismantle the supercharger, the plug bearing the "Mercédès star" and which closes the opening of the starting handle is removed first, after which the connection between the supercharger and the crankshaft is disconnected by applying a spanner to the keyed hub screwed into the crankshaft. The securing bolt, which has a right-handed screw thread, must be given a few turns, whereby the collar of this bolt is brought into contact with the internal annular nut. On giving further turns, the keyed hub is then withdrawn from the crankshaft. The five securing nuts, by means of which the supercharger is attached to the engine casing, are then unscrewed from the top of the supercharger by means of a socket spanner, and the whole supercharger can then be removed in an upward

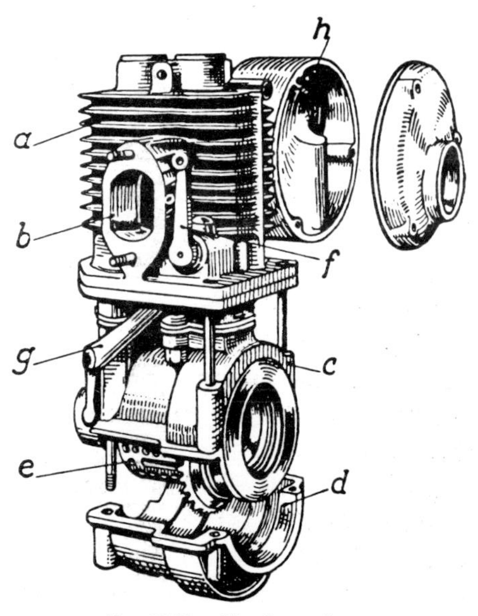

FIG. 1161.—The Supercharger.

a, Blower casing.
b, Compressed air-supply union.
c, Supercharger clutch housing.
d, Clutch housing cover.
f, Operating lever for supercharger.
g, Bell-crank gear for clutch operation.
h, Silencer with worm.
i, Supercharger clutch.

direction, after the pipe with cooling ribs which leads from the supercharger to the carburettor, as well as the complete oil piping and control rod gear, have been disconnected.

If it is now intended to disconnect the supercharger clutch from the supercharger itself, the two long nuts and two short nuts, by means of which the clutch casing is secured, are unscrewed and the clutch casing is lifted off. The interior of the supercharger can be exposed to view, with its vanes and spur gearing, by removing the two countersunk screws and taking off the cover. Both the upper part of the supercharger and the bottom part—which contains the driving gear—can then easily be taken to pieces separately, and the bearings as well as the gear-wheels can then be overhauled.

It is then also possible to remove and clean the plates of the clutch and brake gear.

When assembling these parts, it is necessary not to forget that the clutch must contain twenty-one pairs of plates and the clutch brake nine pairs of plates. When fitting in these parts again, the plates must be inserted in their corresponding grooves in the order of the numbers stamped on them, 1, (2), 3, 1, (2), 3, etc., and it should be noted that the plates with interior notches which are fitted on the splined shaft and which are numbered (2) above are, in fact, supplied with no numbers stamped on them. It is useless to look for a missing clutch spring, for the supercharger does not possess such a spring. The pressure required for actuating the clutch is supplied by the driver's foot, when he throws the supercharger into gear, whilst the pressure on the brake is, on the other hand, supplied by the spring of the pedal.

The lubrication of the engine is so clearly shown in the diagram opposite, with its parts lettered, that beyond mentioning that the circulation is worked by the oil pump with distributor o fitted in the lower half of the crank-case and driven from the bottom end of the vertical shaft, being completely immersed in oil, the diagram explains itself. The horizontal shaft of the pump is driven from above by worm wheel. One of the ends of this main shaft carries the fresh oil pump, as the system, though working under high-pressure circulation, has also an additional supply of fresh oil given to it. This

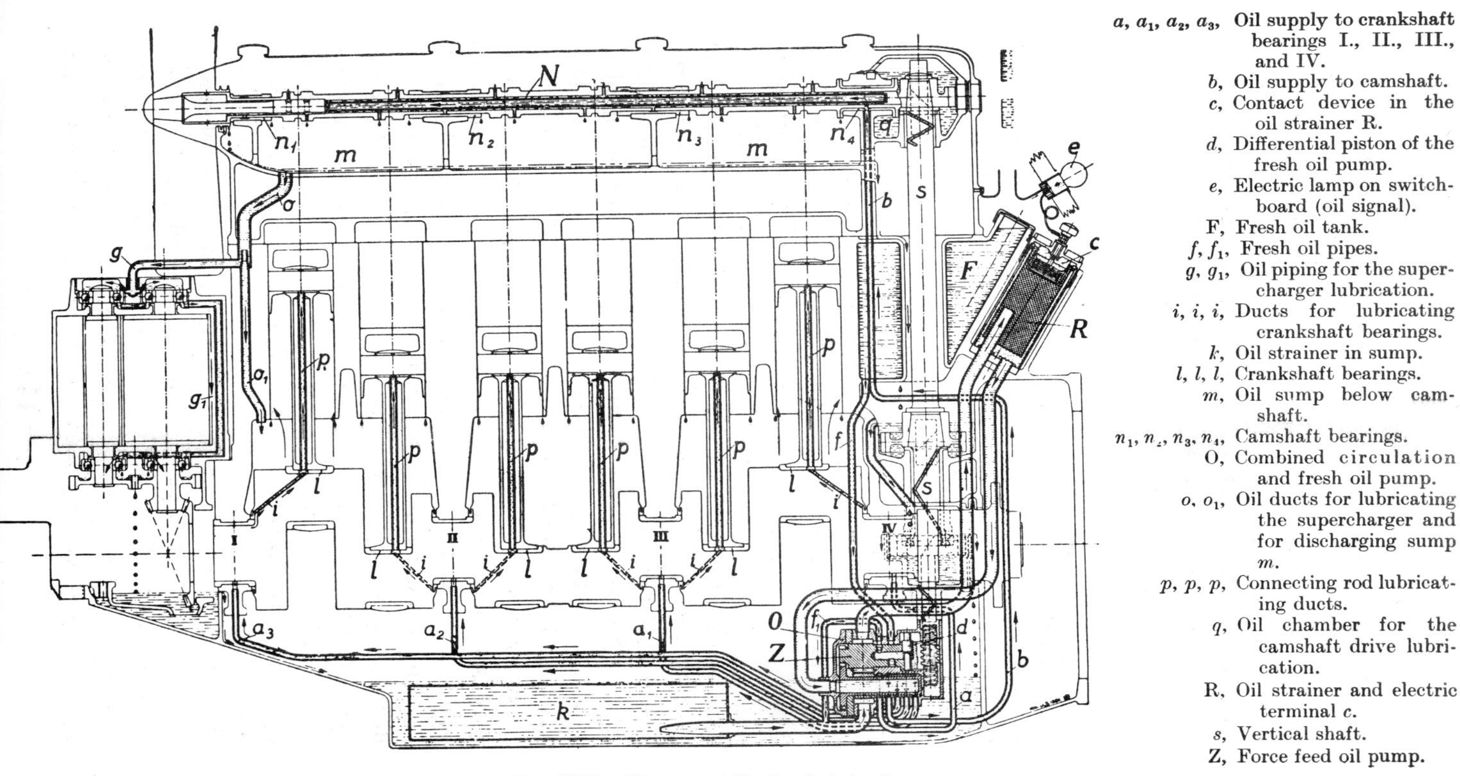

a, a_1, a_2, a_3,	Oil supply to crankshaft bearings I., II., III., and IV.
b,	Oil supply to camshaft.
c,	Contact device in the oil strainer R.
d,	Differential piston of the fresh oil pump.
e,	Electric lamp on switchboard (oil signal).
F,	Fresh oil tank.
f, f_1,	Fresh oil pipes.
g, g_1,	Oil piping for the supercharger lubrication.
i, i, i,	Ducts for lubricating crankshaft bearings.
k,	Oil strainer in sump.
l, l, l,	Crankshaft bearings.
m,	Oil sump below camshaft.
n_1, n_2, n_3, n_4,	Camshaft bearings.
O,	Combined circulation and fresh oil pump.
o, o_1,	Oil ducts for lubricating the supercharger and for discharging sump m.
p, p, p,	Connecting rod lubricating ducts.
q,	Oil chamber for the camshaft drive lubrication.
R,	Oil strainer and electric terminal c.
s,	Vertical shaft.
Z,	Force feed oil pump.

FIG. 1162.—Diagram of Engine Lubrication.

fresh oil pump is a valveless pump, with differential piston *d* moving diametrically, and the other end the geared rotary pump Z, the purpose of which is to force the oil through the circuit in such a manner that one of the gears is fitted on the main shaft, whilst in the hollow spindle of the other gear-wheel is fitted a distributing device which rotates with a comparatively low number of revolutions. The purpose of this distributor is to force circulation oil mixed with fresh oil in definitely measured quantities, in rotation, to each of the parts which require lubrication. In the past the lubrication of supercharged engines and of the supercharger has been the difficulty with which the automobile engineer has had to contend and overcome. Therefore, as this Mercédès supercharged system is a practical solution of the matter, these details are given to enable the reader to know how it has been accomplished.

At each revolution of the main pump shaft the geared pump draws a quantity of circulation oil from the strainer box K in the sump of the crank-case, while the differential piston pump draws a quantity of fresh oil from the fresh oil tank *f*. This supply of fresh oil is then forced through pipe *f* into the oil circuit. The mixed oil supply is then forced upwards to the oil strainer R fitted on the right-hand rear engine lug, flows through the filtering insertion of this strainer, whence it returns in a clean condition to the oil pump and the hollow distributor spindle.

In the hollow spindle of the second gear-wheel is inserted a second hollow distributor spindle, which is also rotated by the pump gear-wheel of the main shaft, although its pinion has one more tooth than the pinion fitted on the hollow distributor spindle. Both hollow spindles perform, consequently, motions which are differential in respect to each other. The slots provided on the periphery of these spindles open and close, therefore, in succession, the ports of the ducts leading to the various parts to be lubricated in such a manner that these parts receive one after the other a full supply of oil, although several parts cannot be supplied simultaneously.

For the lubrication of the supercharger, the oil which flows back from the cylinder head reaches the upper bearings of the blower vanes through a pipe *g*. From this point it proceeds through the duct *g* towards the lower bearings, and the spur gearing of the blower lubricates the ball bearings of the supercharger clutch and the driving bevel gearing, and eventually flows back to the bottom part of the crank-case.

Bosch magneto, dynamo, and starter are used, which have already been dealt with, the particular magneto model being the Bosch Z.H.6 (see p. 484, Vol. II.).

For the timing of these supercharged engines the periphery of the fly-wheel is provided with a set of marks for the

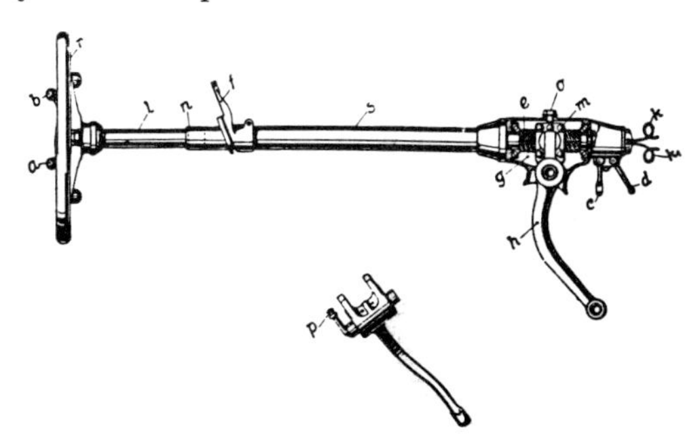

FIG. 1163.—Steering Gear.

a, Throttle lever.
b, Ignition lever.
c, Pivoted lever of mixture adjustment device.
d, Pivoted throttle lever.
e, Screw thread of steering spindle.
f, Bracket for securing steering pillar.
g, Steering pillar.
h, Forked steering lever.
k, k_1, Cables of Bosch horn and dimming device.
l, Steering spindle.
m, Steering nut.
n, Steering spindle bearing.
o, Threaded plug for steering gear lubrication.
p, Fork steering lever lubricator.
r, Steering wheel.
s, Steering pillar.

adjustment of the valves and of the ignition, but also, with a view to facilitate the accurate meshing of the gears when refitting after dismantling each pair of gears which is intended to co-operate, one tooth of one wheel and two adjoining teeth of the opposite wheel are provided with punch marks. If the engine has been properly fitted up, the mark on the one wheel must fit exactly between the two marks on the other wheel. The markings on the fly-wheel are visible after removal of a screwed plug at the rear of the engine casing when the fly-wheel is turned over. The T.D.C. of the pistons in cylinders Nos. 1 and 6, then 5 and 2, and lastly 3 and 4, is indicated by the mark T.P. 1/6, T.P. 5/2, and T.P. 3/4 punched into the periphery of the fly-wheel. This also carries a mark F.Z., indicating the position of the piston in cylinder No. 1 at the point of maximum advanced ignition. When the latter mark makes its appearance in the peep-hole, figure 1 must simultaneously appear in the window of the magneto.

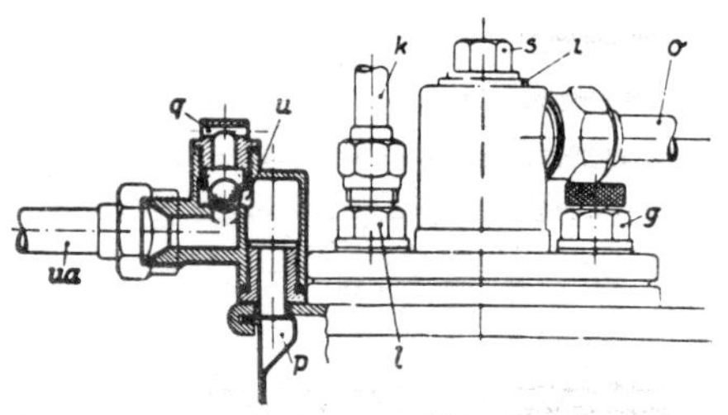

FIG. 1164.—Arrangement of Non-Return Valve on Autovac.

There is no need for special instructions regarding the steering gear, as Fig. 1163 shows the details, which conform to standard practice.

The turn-buckles, of which the pedal brake has four and the hand brake two, are provided to give easy adjustment to the brakes and tighten up the traction cables where necessary.

A special type of autovac is fitted on the Mercédès made by the Pallas Carburettor Co. (Pallas Apparat. A.G.), who

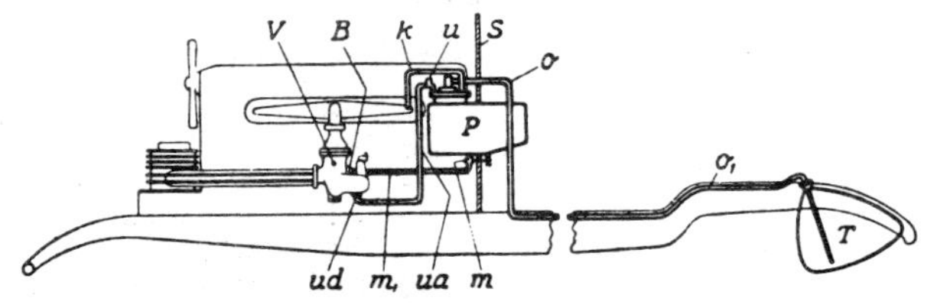

FIG. 1165.—Connections of the Carburettor and of the Fuel Tank with the Autovac.

B, Fuel inlet to carburettor.
g, Air-inlet valve.
k, Vacuum connection with engine induction pipe.
l, Vacuum valve.
m, Fuel supply cut-off cock.
m_1, Fuel supply pipe from autovac to carburettor.
o, o_1, Fuel supply pipe from petrol tank to autovac.
p, Ventilation slot with annular disc.
P, Pallas autovac.
q, Air vent.
s, Strainer locking nut.
S, Dashboard.
T, Fuel tank.
u, Non-return valve from air vent.
ua, Pipe leading from carburettor to air vent.
ud, Union of the carburettor with pipe *ua*.
V, Carburettor.

also make the carburettor. Fig. 1166 shows the vertical section through this. When the supercharger is not in use its action is the same as the ordinary autovac. When the supercharger is engaged, pressure is raised in the autovac through a branched pipe on the blower induction pipe.

Consequently, the autovac thereupon automatically becomes a pressure tank instead of a vacuum tank, but only so long as the supercharger is engaged. The ventilation duct *p*, with

a, Outer container.

b, Petrol suction chamber.

c, Bottom part of outer container.

d, Fuel valve.

e, Float.

f, Oscillating float levers.

g, Air-inlet valve.

h, Link for working air valve.

i, Strainer chamber.

k, Vacuum connection to induction pipe.

l, Vacuum valve.

m, Petrol supply cock.

n, Inner fuel-supply pipe.

o, Fuel-inlet pipe from tank.

p, Ventilation slot with annular duct.

q, Ventilation plug.

r, Cover ring.

s, Strainer screw.

t, Water trap.

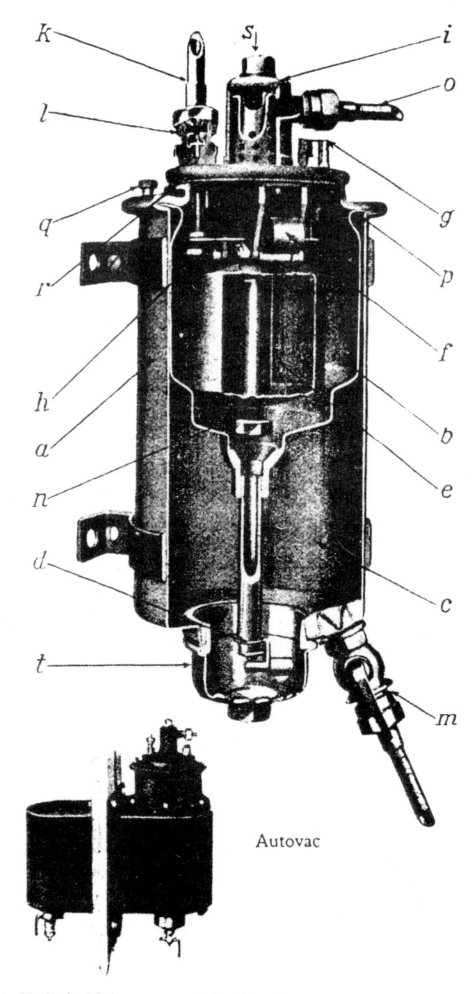

Method of fixing autovac to dashboard.

Fig. 1166.—Pallas Autovac.

the annular channel of the apparatus, is connected with the air pipe *ua*, which leads to the carburettor through a non-return valve *u*, by means of which either the air pipe or ventilation plug *q* can be closed. (See illustration, Fig. 1164, p. 1494.)

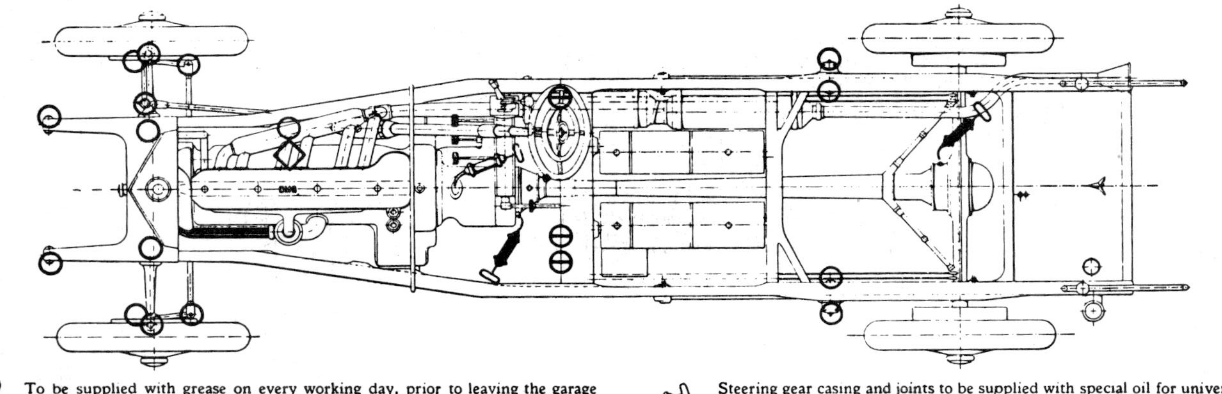

FIG. 1167.—Lubrication Diagram.

M.G. (Morris Garages)

FOUR AND SIX CYLINDERS

THE M.G. Car Company of Oxford make two models, both sports cars, though also provided with enclosed coachwork. The four-cylinder has a bore of 75 mm. and stroke of 102 mm., and is usually styled the 14-40 H.P. model, mark IV. The engine tappet clearances when warm are inlet ·004 in. and exhaust ·006 in., and the valve timing is :—

Inlet opens	12½° before T.D.C.
Inlet closes	22½° after B.D.C.
Exhaust opens . . .	36½° before B.D.C.
Exhaust closes	14° after T.D.C.

The oil pressure of the engine, when warm, at a road speed of 40 miles per hour is 4 lbs. per square inch, and when idling, 2 lbs. The firing order of the cylinders is 1, 3, 4, 2, and the Lucas magneto contact point gap is ·025 in. Solex carburettor is provided and Lucas 12-volt lighting set with a 63 amp.-hour battery. The dynamo gives a charging rate of 8 amps. The clutch pedal clearance is 1 in., and the brakes have rod adjustments. Only two rings are fitted on the pistons, which have a clearance of 12 mm.

The six-cylinder model has a bore of 69 mm. and a stroke of 110 mm., rated at 17·7 H.P., the firing order of the engine being 1, 5, 3, 6, 2, 4, and the tappet clearances, both inlet and exhaust when the engine is warm, are ·004 in. The valve timing is :—

Inlet opens	7½° before T.D.C.
Inlet closes	50½° after B.D.C.
Exhaust opens	41½° before B.D.C.
Exhaust closes	16½° after T.D.C.

The oil pressures shown on the gauge when engine is warm, at 50 miles per hour road speed, should be 40 lbs. per square inch, and when engine is idling, 5 to 10 lbs. per square inch. The piston clearance is 11 mm. with three rings. Lucas R4 type coil ignition is fitted, which has both hand and automatic advance. The contact point gap is ·020 in. Twin SU carburettor is fitted on this model, with Lucas 12-volt lighting and 75 amp.-hour battery, the dynamo having a charging rate

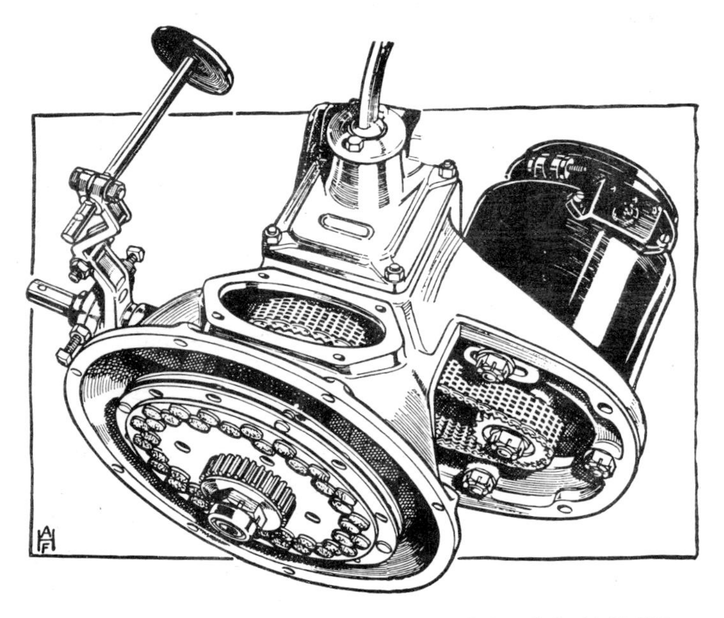

Fig. 1209.—Details of Clutch and Dynamotor Drive of the 14-40 H.P. Four-Cylinder M.G.

of approximately 12 amps. The instructions in regard to overhaul are somewhat similar to those already detailed on the various Morris cars, so beyond showing in Fig. 1209 details of the clutch and dynamotor drive, these apply generally.

To adjust the dynamotor driving chain, remove cover-plate at forward end of dynamotor and, with a special crank spanner (included in tool kit), loosen the nuts inside the case which locks the dynamotor in position. The whole dynamotor can be moved to tighten or loosen the chain;

when tension is correct, there should be a maximum up and down play of about ½ in., and this should be tested in several positions in case there is a " tight spot." Great care must be taken to ensure that the dynamotor is tightly locked in position after adjustment.

Note.—A loose dynamotor chain is often responsible for a rumbling noise which appears to come from the front of the engine, and is frequently erroneously attributed to noisy timing wheels.

RILEY

FOUR AND SIX CYLINDER

THE four-cylinder 9 H.P. Riley has a bore and stroke of 60·3 × 95·2 mm. respectively, giving a cubic capacity of 1,087 c.c. The engine rating is 9·01 H.P. (taxed as 9 H.P., as any fractions being less than one-tenth do not count under the present Treasury rating for taxation purposes). The tappet clearances when warm are inlet ·002 in. and

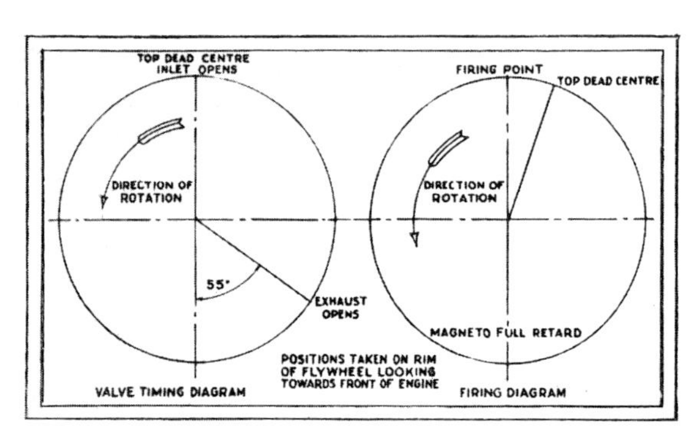

FIG. 1240.—Valve Timing and Firing Diagram.

exhaust ·006 in., while the order of firing of the cylinders is 1, 2, 4, 3. The valve timing is as follows :—

Inlet opens	At T.D.C.
Inlet closes	50° after B.D.C.
Exhaust opens	55° before B.D.C.
Exhaust closes	30° after T.D.C.

The oil pressure when the car is travelling, 40 to 60 lbs. per square inch, should be indicated on the gauge. Wakefield's Castrol XL is recommended. The capacity of the crank-case is 1 gal., the radiator and water connections

$2\frac{1}{2}$ gals., and the petrol tank $5\frac{1}{2}$ gals. The piston clearances are ·003 in. at skirt and ·0012 in. at the top, four rings are fitted.

B.T.H. or M.L. magnetos will be found on the 9 H.P. Riley for the ignition, with a hand advance of 15° and no automatic advance. The contact points gap should be ·0012 in. A 12-volt Rotax lighting set and battery is given in the equipment, the battery having a capacity of 44 amp.-hours, the dynamo charging at 8 amps. when the car is proceeding at 20 miles an hour on top gear.

The clutch - pedal clearance is $3\frac{3}{4}$ in.

A Zenith carburettor is fitted on the standard and 2 S.U.'s on the sports models.

As will be seen from Fig. 1241, there are no chains or belt drives which need tightening on this 9 H.P. Riley engine, as all the drives are positive with helical gears, and their lubrication is automatically arranged. The dynamo is direct and the speedometer is gear driven, the first from the front of the crankshaft and the latter by worm gear off the propeller shaft. To examine the timing wheels, 14 nuts have to be removed, and Fig. 1241 shows the engine with this cover removed.

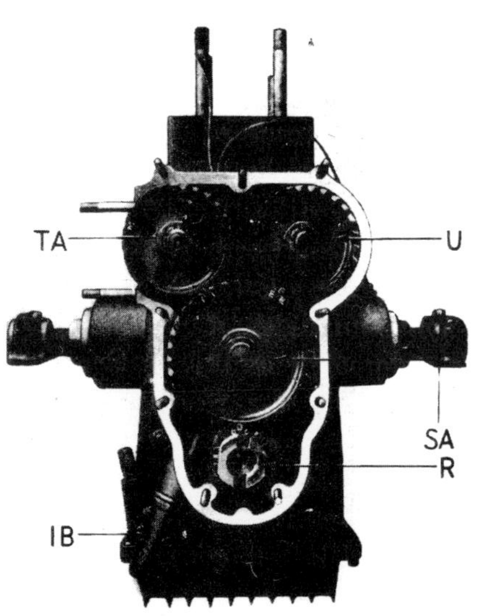

Fig. 1241.—Camshaft, Dynamo, and Magneto Drive.

To check the magneto timing, first rotate the engine until the contact breaker points are just separating, with the distributor arm over No. 1 and the ignition control lever on steering column fully retarded. The engine should now be slightly before T.D.C., which can be checked after removing the cover by the marks on the fly-wheel (see Fig. 1242). On no account must the ignition be advanced further than this or it will be firing too early. If the timing is incorrect pull the engine over until T.D.C. mark is as shown in Fig. 1240, p. 1616, valve timing and firing diagram, and then unlock the three magneto clamp bolts and twist the magneto round until the points are just separating, although only a small adjustment of half a tooth in the pinion is thus obtainable. The marks on the fly-wheel relate to No. 1 cylinder, which is nearest to the radiator. The valve timing is as given in Fig. 1240, p. 1616, and the T.D.C. is marked on the fly-wheel. All the timing gears are stamped so that they can be easily reset, as shown in Fig. 1241. The crankshaft

Fig. 1242.—Fly-Wheel and Gear-Box.

should be set with the slot vertical and the gear R stamped at the top with the two O's which register with the tooth similarly marked on the intermediate wheel SA. The cam-shaft wheels mesh with this and are marked U and TA, as shown in Fig. 1241, and are stamped E and I respectively, the latter driving the magneto pinion. In the centre of each camshaft is a four-lobed cam, operating on a spring-loaded plunger, which is so designed as to level up the torque on the shaft, and the thrust from the helical gears is taken on the ball bearings. The tooth of the magneto pinion, which meshes with the one stamped M on the cam-shaft, can be identified by a dot which is stamped upon it.

The details of the plate clutch are shown in Fig. 1243, and consist of a single fabric-covered plate acting between the fly-wheel face and sliding member. The clutch withdrawal mechanism operates through the shaft and toggles to the housing in which the thrust race ZB is fitted. The latter has to be lubricated, as well as the sliding pins, with gear oil occasionally. The illustration also shows the starter pinion. On no account oil the helix drive for the starter pinion, as the oil only collects the dust and grit, which results in the pinion being jammed. It might be occasionally slightly smeared with graphite or black lead if any lubricant at all is required. The clutch-pedal levers when not in use should be clear of the thrust face, but as the clutch lining gets worn the pedal stands further away from the board, and should be adjusted by means of screwed link. One serration moves the pedal $1\frac{7}{8}$ in.

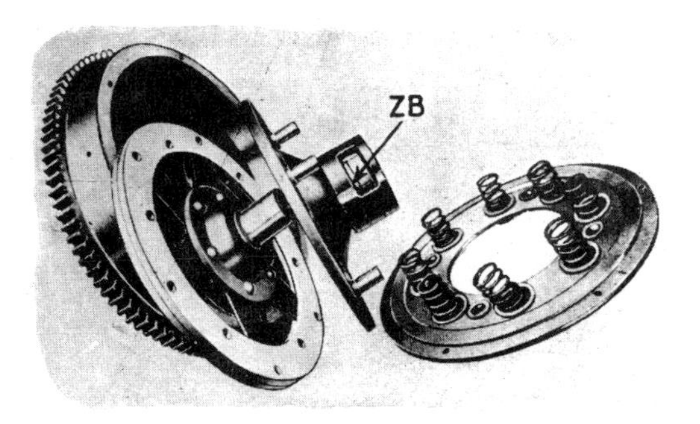

FIG. 1243.—Clutch Dissembled.

The four-speed gear-box has the third-speed wheels also in constant mesh besides the usual constant and is of helical tooth form to give silence in operation. The main shafts run on ball bearings. The gear-box holds about $2\frac{1}{2}$ pints of oil and the filler is situated on the left-hand side, placed at a height so that it cannot be overfilled.

The six-cylinder Riley, styled the 14 H.P., is actually rated at 13·515 H.P. and has the same bore and stroke, tappet clearances, piston clearances, while the order of firing of the cylinders is 1, 5, 3, 6, 2, 4. The valve timing is also identical with the four-cylinder, as well as the oil pressures. The engine crank-case, however, holds $1\frac{1}{2}$ gals. of oil, the radiator and water jackets $3\frac{1}{2}$ gals., and the petrol tank 12 gals. No magneto is fitted on this model, but the usual Delco-Remy

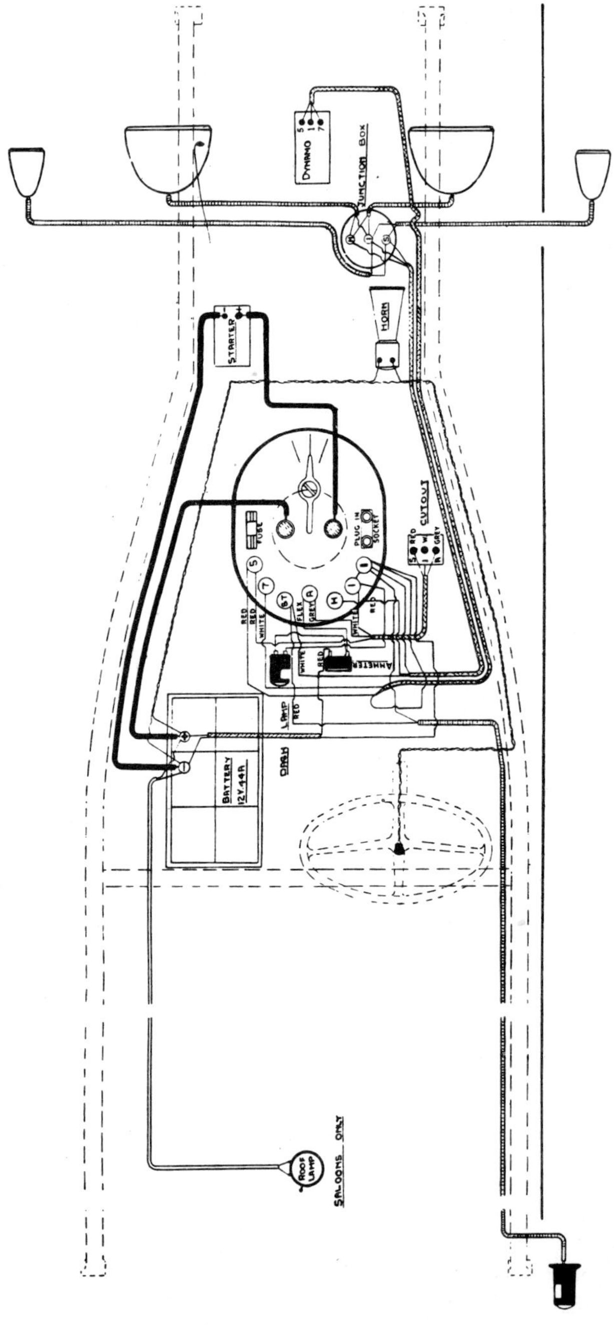

Fig. 1244.—Wiring Diagram.

coil ignition having an automatic advance of 10°, hand advance of 15°, making a total maximum ignition advance of 25°. Delco-Remy ignition has been treated so many times previously that no further reference in regard thereto is necessary. The lighting and battery is a 12-volt system made by the Rotax Company, and the battery capacity is 66 amp.-hours. These batteries are carried in two units of 6 volts each, wired series, situated each side of the propeller shaft under the rear seats of the vehicle.

Both the 9 H.P. and 14 H.P. Rileys have semi-floating spiral bevel rear axles, with axle shaft (six spline N.C.S.), oil capacity of casing 3 to $3\frac{1}{2}$ pints. The adjustment of the bevel pinion is by a screwed sleeve accessible from the top of crown gear housing.

In filling hub bearings, remove plug in hub, then fill through greaser by means of a gun until the surplus oil flows out of the plug hole, so that the oil is not forced into the brakes.

To make steering rake adjustment, loosen clamp holding column to frame, and also the clamp on the instrument board. If a large adjustment of angle is made—there is a 4-in. movement measured at wheel—it may be necessary to slightly adjust the controls, but no special notes are required for this.

On the 14 H.P. model only it is necessary to remove the board in the luggage space to get at the rear axle oil filler; use inspection lamp and long tun-dish. The oil filler cap is removable from rear by reaching under petrol tank.

For brake adjustment, the Riley "Nine" mark III. has compensated rod adjustment, which can be effected by means of a wing-nut under the floor boards, whereas the Riley "Nine" mark IV. has cables instead of rods, and the adjustment can be done by hand from the driver's seat, being above the floor boards. The six-cylinder is similar to mark IV.

A Zenith triple diffuser carburettor is sometimes fitted on the 14 H.P. Riley, and the usual best setting is choke 19, main 95, and compensator slightly larger.

It will be found, however, that some models are equipped with double S.U. carburettors.

With regard to the rear axle, fitters should not attempt to remove the hub from the shaft, as this is driven on. If the drive case requires inspection, the hub and the axle must be removed by unlcck-ing the set-pin and pulling both hub and axle out together. Next remove the rear axle cover, leaving the axle as in Fig. 1245. The caps are screwed inside and each carry a sleeve which can be adjusted, as already stated, so as to locate the bevel wheel in conjunction with the pinion. The central set-pin KB locks these adjusting sleeves. In adjusting these sleeves, remove the locking plate

FIG. 1245.—Rear Axle, showing Pinion Adjustment.

EA (Fig. 1246), and with a tommy bar screw the inner sleeve FA right or left according to the direction which the bevel pinion requires, viz., further into or out of mesh with the wheel. When the correct position is obtained, replace lock-plate EA into slot in sleeve FA. As there are twenty slots in the pinion housing, it can be very finely adjusted to within two or three thousandths of an inch, so a repairer should have no difficulty in making this rear axle silent in its operation.

FIG. 1246.—Pinion Adjustment.

CB, Two pivot pin nuts at rear of brake carrier which, when undone and pins removed, permit the brake shoes to be taken out for relining.
FA, Inner sleeve.
EA, Locking plate.

On Colonial models of Riley " Nines " a fan is fitted which is driven by a belt from the left-hand camshaft. It is mounted on an eccentric for adjusting the tension of the belt.

ROLLS-ROYCE

SIX CYLINDERS

Two chassis are built by Rolls-Royce Limited, of Derby. The 20 H.P. model has six cylinders in line vertical, 3 in. bore × 4½ in. stroke, and a rating of 21·6 H.P., the cylinders being cast in one block, with separate detachable head carrying overhead valves and rocker levers, operated by push-rods from a camshaft in the crank-case. Inlet and exhaust valves are interchangeable. The 40-50 H.P. six-cylinder Rolls-Royce has also its six cylinders in line vertical, with a 4¼ in. bore × 5½ in. stroke, but the cylinders are cast in two groups of three, arranged with separate detachable aluminium alloy "turbulent" head carrying overhead valves and rocker mechanism, also operated by push-rods from the camshaft in the crankshaft, and the inlet and exhaust valves are interchangeable bronze valve seats screwed into head. Both these chassis have carburettors of Rolls-Royce patented design of the two-jet type with automatic air valve, and a separate small carburettor incorporated to ensure easy and positive start when the engine is cold. On the 40-50 H.P. six-cylinder model, which is rated at 43·3 H.P., the throttle valve is controlled by means of a centrifugal governor, which can be adjusted so as to maintain any constant speed of the engine. The throttle valve can be held open when desired by means of a pedal.

Both of these chassis have engine lubrication under high pressure by a gear type of oil pump to all bearings of the crankshaft connecting rods and gudgeon pins. The pump also delivers oil under low pressure to the timing wheel case and overhead valve gear. The steering of these chassis is of the special Rolls-Royce worm and nut type with universal ball joints to all steering connections enclosed in leather covers. The rear axle is of the full floating type, the driving shafts carrying no load except the drive, with spiral bevel gears used for the final drive, the differential gear being also of the bevel type for the 20 H.P. and the spur-gear type for the 40-50 H.P. chassis.

For the 20 H.P. chassis, two pairs of brakes operating on drums attached to rear wheel hubs, one pair operated by the pedal and one pair by the hand lever, are found on some of the older models, though later cars are fitted with the Rolls-Royce patent design four wheel brakes operated by the pedal, with an entirely independent set of brakes fitted to the rear wheels operated by hand. The latter are also fitted on the 40-50 H.P. six-cylinder New Phantom chassis. This is usually styled the Rolls-Royce patent six-brake system.

The ignition system on the 20 H.P. chassis is battery and induction coil with ballast resistance and low-tension make and break, combined with high-tension jump-spark distributor and automatic advance by means of centrifugal governor. A high-tension magneto is also provided as a stand-by. The 40-50 H.P. model is similarly equipped. A 12-volt system is provided for the electrical installation.

The order of firing of the cylinders is the same for both of these engines, viz., 1, 4, 2, 6, 3, 5, and the tappet clearances when cold for inlet and exhaust are ·006 in. for 40-50 H.P. and ·003 in. for 20 H.P.

The valve timings with tappet clearance of ·020 in. are :—

	20 H.P.	40-50 H.P.
Inlet opens	At T.D.C.	14° after T.D.C.
Inlet closes	44°	30° after B.D.C.
Exhaust opens	48°	34° before B.D.C.
Exhaust closes	12°	2° before T.D.C.

The radiator has a cooling capacity of 460 sq. in. and the petrol tank holds 14 gals. for the 20 H.P. A Watford magneto is fitted as well as the Rolls-Royce coil, both having a hand advance of 40° and automatic advance, with coil only, of 30°. The contact points gap is ·012 in. The dynamo charging rate is 10 amps.

For the 40-50 H.P. Rolls-Royce the radiator has a cooling surface of 588 sq. in. and the petrol tank holds 20 gals. The ignition has a hand advance of 20° and an automatic

Fig. 1247.—New Phantom Rolls-Royce Carburettor in Position on Engine.

advance of 30°, giving a total maximum ignition advance of 50°, and the 12-volt battery has a 75 amp.-hour capacity, with a dynamo charging rate of 11 to 12 amps. The maximum gap opening, in setting the contact points for both models, should be ·017 to ·021 in.

The Rolls-Royce automatic expanding type carburettor is provided with two jets controlled by a single lever from the instrument board. Each of these jets is located in a venturi tube, the smaller one always being in action and the larger one being automatically brought into action by an increase beyond a certain value in the depression existing

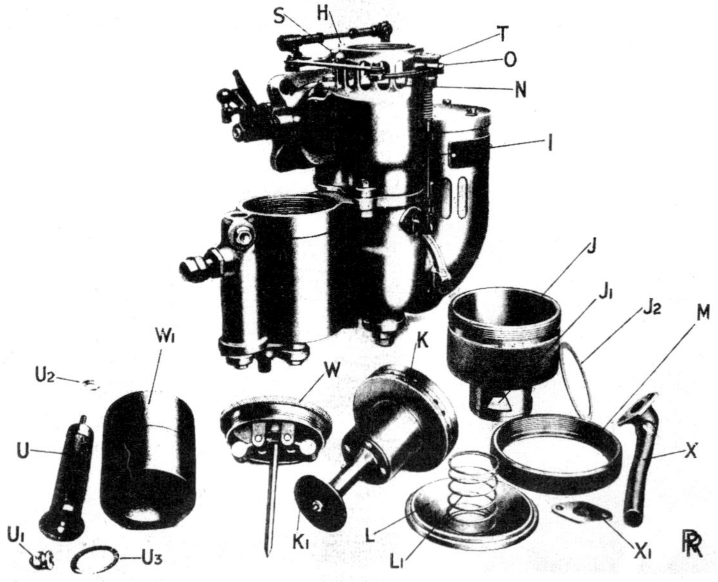

FIG. 1248.—Carburettor with Certain Parts Dismantled.

within the carburettor, due to an increase in engine speed or throttle opening, or both. As both the 40 H.P. and the 20 H.P. carburettors are of similar design, the larger one is illustrated here. The outlets of the jets are regulated by tapered needle valves, that for the small or low-speed jet being shown at H, and the control for the large or high-speed jet needle at I. The automatic expanding effect is attained by the provision of a suction-operated piston working in a cylinder J located above the high-speed jet. The cylinder J and piston K are shown removed for cleaning in Fig. 1248.

The cap L carrying the spring L_1 fits over the top of the cylinder and is retained by the knurled nut M. Increased depression in the carburettor raises the piston K against the spring L_1 carrying with it a diaphragm K_1 which fits into and in its lowest position blanks off the larger choke tube. The lifting of this diaphragm admits air past the high-speed jet. More movement of the piston not only opens the high-speed choke tube still further, but also admits air by uncovering the ports J_1, the air gaining admission through ports N in

FIG. 1249.—Adjusting the Tappets of 20 H.P. Rolls-Royce Engine.
C, Position for measuring tappet clearance with gauge.

the carburettor, thereby counteracting the tendency for the mixture to become over-rich at increased air velocity. After cleaning the air valve and cylinder, when necessary, care should be taken when replacing the chamber J to see that the metal washer J_2 is in position and that the joint faces are perfectly clean.

If the adjustment of the jet needles has been upset for any reason, it can be restored in the following manner :—

With the mixture control lever set half-way along its quadrant and the clamping screws O of the jet needle levers slack, each of the knurled nuts S and P should be turned until the line filed across them registers with the line across the end of the corresponding screwed spindle, the end of the spindle being at the same time flush with the end of the nut. The clamping screw should then be tightened and the setting as originally made by the makers will have been restored. If, however, owing to damaged and replaced parts, it becomes necessary to reset the jets with no guide in the form of markings referred to, the following procedure should be adopted :—

With the mixture control lever set half-way along its quadrant and the clamping screws slack, the knurled nuts should be turned until both jets are fully closed. In the case of the high-speed jet, this will occur when its nut T is turned in a clockwise direction as far as possible, the fingers only being used in this operation and no undue force being applied. For the low-speed jet the knurled nut S should be turned in a clockwise direction until its lower side just commences to lift away from the facing against which it normally rests. Both jets will now be fully closed. A trial setting can then be obtained by rotating the knurled nuts in an anti-clockwise direction, two and a half turns being given to that of the high-speed jet, and that of the low-speed jet being rotated slightly over three-quarters of a turn. The clamping screws should then be tightened and the engine started.

With the mixture control lever in its central position, the governor lever should be set to run the engine at a speed at which the automatic piston valve only just commences to lift. Movement of this can be observed by looking through the air ports in the carburettor. The clamping screw of the low-speed jet needle should then be slackened and the knurled nut turned in a clockwise direction until the engine speed becomes slightly reduced. If, with the governor lever set to run the engine at a slow speed and the mixture control lever in the middle of its quadrant, there is a tendency for the engine to " hunt " on the governor, this is an indication that the low-speed jet is reduced too much. It should, therefore, be increased slightly until the engine runs steadily and at a reasonable slow speed when warm. The clamping screw should then be tightened and the mixture control lever moved first over to " Strong " and then to " Weak." If, in both of these positions, the engine misses fire, or even possibly stops, then the adjustment of this jet is fairly correct. To test the high-speed jet setting, the ignition should be fully advanced, using both battery and magneto ignitions, and the engine " raced " by opening the throttle by hand. Care must be taken that this is done only momentarily, and that a

Fig. 1250.—Cylinder Head on 20 H.P. Rolls-Royce Engine Removed for Decarbonising.

dangerous speed is not attained. At the same time, the mixture control lever should be again moved first over to " Strong " and then to " Weak," in both of which positions a decided faltering of the engine should be apparent, accompanied by " popping back " through the carburettor in the " Weak " position.

The foregoing will only provide a preliminary setting to be modified or confirmed by a road test.

On the 40-50 H.P. Rolls, the high-speed jet comes into operation at about 7 miles per hour on top gear on the level, consequently any sign of too rich or too weak a mixture below this speed is an indication that the low-speed jet

FIG. 1251.—Ignition Coil and Distributor on 20 H.P. Rolls-Royce.

Ib, Head from coil to distributor.
Tm, Single high-tension head from magneto to distributor (holder on the ignition tower).
W, Coil.
X, Combined low-tension contact breaker.
X_1, High-tension distributor.
X_2, Condenser.
Z, Lubricator.

requires adjustment. At speeds above 7 miles an hour, the high-speed jet has an increasing influence over the mixture.

For the 20 H.P. model the high-speed jet comes into operation at about 4 miles an hour at top gear on the level, so the same remarks apply to the setting of that carburettor, but at the reduced speed.

A small auxiliary carburettor is provided for starting purposes only. This is arranged on the induction pipe, as shown at v in Fig. 1247, p. 1625, and controlled from the instrument board. A small lever is mounted on the latter, its dial being marked "On" and "Off" to the left and right respectively. A spring-controlled piston is operated by engine suction and regulates the air supply to suit the degree of this suction as in the main carburettor. The petrol supply can be adjusted by rotating the screw v_1 at the top of the starting carburettor, which carries a taper jet needle. Screwing this down weakens the starting mixture, and conversely unscrewing it enriches the mixture. Adjustment of the starting carburettor should only be made when the engine is cold. If necessary to clean out the float chamber, unscrew the cover w and remove the float w_1. The crank-case breather pipe is led to the carburettor air inlet, as can be seen at x in Fig. 1247, and is shown removed in Fig. 1248. A small gauze x_1 is arranged between the pipe flange and the carburettor, which has to be cleaned from time to time. In ordinary circumstances, if the carburettor really requires thorough overhauling and cleaning, it should be removed from the engine and the lower portion—including the float chamber and air inlet—should be detached. To do this, the main petrol supply union must first be disconnected from the float chamber, preferably by removing the whole pipe, a union being provided just under the dashboard. The petrol supply pipe to the starting carburettor must also be disconnected. Then the controls should be uncoupled, in the case of the mixture control by removing the pin from the lower arm of the lever carried on the air inlet, and in the case of the throttle by pulling off the ball joint from the throttle lever. The throttle spring should also be disconnected and the crank-case breather pipe removed. The four nuts securing the carburettor to the induction branch can next be unscrewed and the carburettor removed.

It must be particularly noticed that before attempting to detach the float chamber from the carburettor, the low-speed jet needle must be taken out, otherwise it will almost certainly be damaged. It is easily removed, after taking away the air valve and chamber, by disconnecting the two control connections to its lever and unscrewing the two countersunk set-screws on top of the carburettor. The jet needle may then be lifted out complete, its lever, adjusting nut, bearing, and spring, the lever not being disturbed from its setting on the knurled adjusting nut. The high-speed jet control mechanism must also be disconnected by removing pin from jaw at the lower end of the rod I. The three nuts which hold the two main portions of the carburettor body together may then be unscrewed, and the lower portion removed by carefully lowering it until the choke tubes are clear.

The high-speed jet needle is removed by taking out the two countersunk set-screws which secure the bearing of its operating lever to the side of the carburettor. This lever, with its bearing, may then be removed, the carburettor body being held the right way up while doing so, otherwise the jet needle may fall out and be damaged.

The plugs below both jets should then be unscrewed and cleaned from sediment ; at the same time, it should be ascertained that the spring plunger below the high-speed jet needle is working quite freely. The upward pressure of this spring is relied upon to open the high-speed jet, therefore its freedom of movement is of great importance. When replacing the parts, care must be taken that the plug containing the spring plunger is fitted below the high-speed jet. The air-valve chamber, the air valve, and the low-speed jet needle should not be replaced until the carburettor body is again complete.

The Rolls-Royce four-wheel braking system comprises a servo motor of the dry disc clutch type, possessing the feature that it is equally available when the car is moving backwards or forwards. Should the servo be out of action, the rear pedal operated brake still provides the same braking capacities as were available on these chassis before the adoption of front wheel brakes.

The points on the system where any adjustment is provided or necessary, are as follows :—

On the rear brakes a serrated adjustment on the cam operating levers, on the front brakes a similar type of adjustment to that on the rear brakes, and on the servo motor a serrated adjusting nut on the end of the servo shaft.

Having removed the floor boards when an adjustment of the rear brakes is required, the pedal should be comparatively lightly depressed by the hand and the servo engaging mechanism watched. It is also advisable during this operation to jack up one of the rear wheels and get some one else to turn the wheels and to indicate when the brakes are applied.

Measuring from the top edge of the pedal towards the dash, the first $\frac{1}{4}$-in. movement will be required to take up the servo clearances, a further $1\frac{1}{8}$-in. movement should just apply the rear brakes, this further movement corresponding to $\frac{5}{8}$ in. of movement at the ends of the levers on the rear axle. In the case of the hand brake the shoes should be just rubbing the drums when the lever is set to the third notch of its quadrant towards the "on" position, this movement corresponding to about $\frac{3}{4}$ in. at the end of the levers on the rear axle. If appreciably more movement than this is required, it will be necessary to utilise the adjustments provided on the rear axle. The mechanisms are enclosed in metal covers to protect them from dust and dirt.

If excessive movement is observed at the end of the cam-operating lever, it is an indication that the front brakes require adjustment. The movement at the end of this lever for correct adjustment should be from $\frac{7}{16}$ to $\frac{1}{2}$ in. when lightly depressed by hand. It should not exceed $\frac{7}{8}$ in. When this figure is exceeded adjustment is imperative.

Another way of checking the clearance is by the movement of the two levers on the axle to which the pull ropes are attached. The corresponding movement here for correct adjustment will be approximately $\frac{5}{8}$ to $\frac{11}{16}$ in., measured at the end of one of the levers.

For the adjustment of the servo, which is of the dry disc clutch type, screw up the nut z (Fig. 1252).

This nut is locked by twenty-five rounded serrations formed

on its face, which engage similar serrations on a washer which is secured against rotation relative to the shaft. The depth of these serrations is proportioned to give the correct clearance on the servo, the nut being turned so that the teeth lightly ride over each other and engage again. On no account should force be used in this operation, as such treatment would nullify the object of the teeth, viz., to ensure the correct clearance with very little trouble.

FIG. 1252.—Servo Motor of Brakes and its Connections.

After effecting adjustment in this way, care should be taken to see that the serrations are properly in engagement. The adjusting nut Z should not be screwed up more than one serration—that is, one twenty-fifth of a turn—without testing the servo adjustment.

To test the servo adjustment, the pedal should be depressed lightly by hand as when testing the rear foot-brake adjustment. But in this case it should only be depressed sufficiently to engage the servo and just short of moving the lever A_2 rotationally. The pedal travel should then not be less than $\frac{1}{4}$ in. measured at the top edge of the pedal towards the dash. It must be realised that this movement is entirely due to the servo clearance and does not alter the rear brake clearances. Hence, lever A_2 is not moved rotationally as mentioned.

Another method of testing for the correct servo clearance is by measuring the gap on the straight or axial sides of the inclined teeth between levers A_1 and A_2. It should be possible to insert a ·025-in. feeler gauge at this point when the servo is engaged lightly. After adjustment, the servo clearance should always be checked again by one or both of the methods explained.

Emphasis is laid on this point as obviously a " dragging " servo, due to abuse of the adjustment provided, will result in " dragging " of the brakes on all wheels.

A single plate type clutch, running dry, is fitted on Rolls Royce cars (see Fig. 1253), the fabric A being secured to the fly-wheel and clutch-ring member respectively (with floating friction ring carrier on the 40-50 H.P. model only), thereby enabling the clutch plate B to be kept as light as possible. The casing C, to which is bolted a clutch plate B, encloses a universal joint through which the drive is taken to the hollow shaft D. The clutch plate is accurately located relative to the fly-wheel friction rings A, owing to the fact that casing C is carried in two ball journals, C_1 and C_2, one on either side of it, within the fly-wheel, axial movement of the plate and casing being allowed in the mounting of these bearings.

A special form of clutch stop or brake is provided, the pressure of which is predetermined and is not directly affected by pressure on the clutch pedal. A coil spring E opposes the action of the main clutch springs, and therefore tends to push the plate B and casing C away from the engine when the clutch is withdrawn. A collar F on the clutch shaft is then caused to make contact with a friction ring G_1, carried on an axially adjustable sleeve G, fixed to the casing.

With regard to adjustments, none is provided for the clutch springs H, these being so proportioned as to render the adjustment unnecessary in the light of the clutch, according to the makers. An adjustment is provided, however, to ensure an equal outward movement being imparted to the clutch ring B_1 by each of the four levers J on withdrawal.

The adjustment of the clutch stop is effected by moving the stationary sleeve G (Fig. 1253) axially nearer to or farther from the collar F. It must be realised, however, that reduction of the clearance between these parts will not necessarily increase the effect of the clutch stop. On the

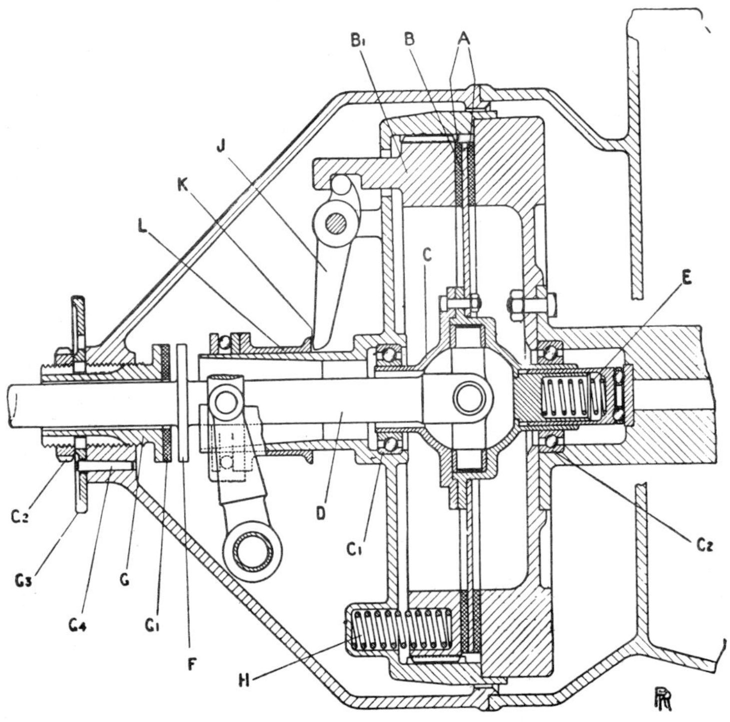

Fig. 1253.—Diagrammatic Sectional Elevation of Clutch.

contrary, it may reduce it, owing to the fact that the clutch plate cannot then move far enough back to clear the front friction ring. Too large a clearance at the clutch stop will have a similar effect, because the spring E will then tend to keep the clutch plate in engagement with the rear friction ring, even on the maximum depression of the pedal.

The best results are usually obtained when there is from ·020 to ·030 in. clearance (engine cold) between the collar F and friction ring G_1 with the clutch engaged. The sleeve

G is screwed into the clutch housing and locked by a serrated nut G_2. The knurled ring G_3 is provided with internal serrations fitting grooves in the thread of sleeve G. It is also drilled with sixteen holes, one of which engages with the dowel-pin G_4. After unlocking and screwing back the nut G_2, so that ring G_3 can be moved backwards clear of the dowel-pin G_4, ring G_3 should be turned with the hand in a direction

FIG. 1254.—The Water Pump.

A, Screw down lubricator.
B, Hole for oiling flexible drive coupling.
C, Packing gland nut.
D, Nut.
E, Coupling.
F, Nut.
G, Pump lubricator.
G_1, Nut securing pump bracket.
H, Bearing.
J, Front packing.
J_1, Rear packing.
K, Ring.

opposite to the direction of rotation of the engine until the friction ring G_1 can be felt to be in contact with collar F.

The correct clearance can then be obtained by turning the knurled ring in the opposite direction to the extent of one-quarter of a turn, equivalent to four of the holes. After pressing it forward so that the dowel-pin G_4 enters one of the holes, the lock-nut G_2 should be retightened

If this does not appear to provide the best setting, judging by the length of time taken by the clutch shaft to come to rest, after declutching with the engine running at a normal slow speed, it will be advisable to proceed as follows :—

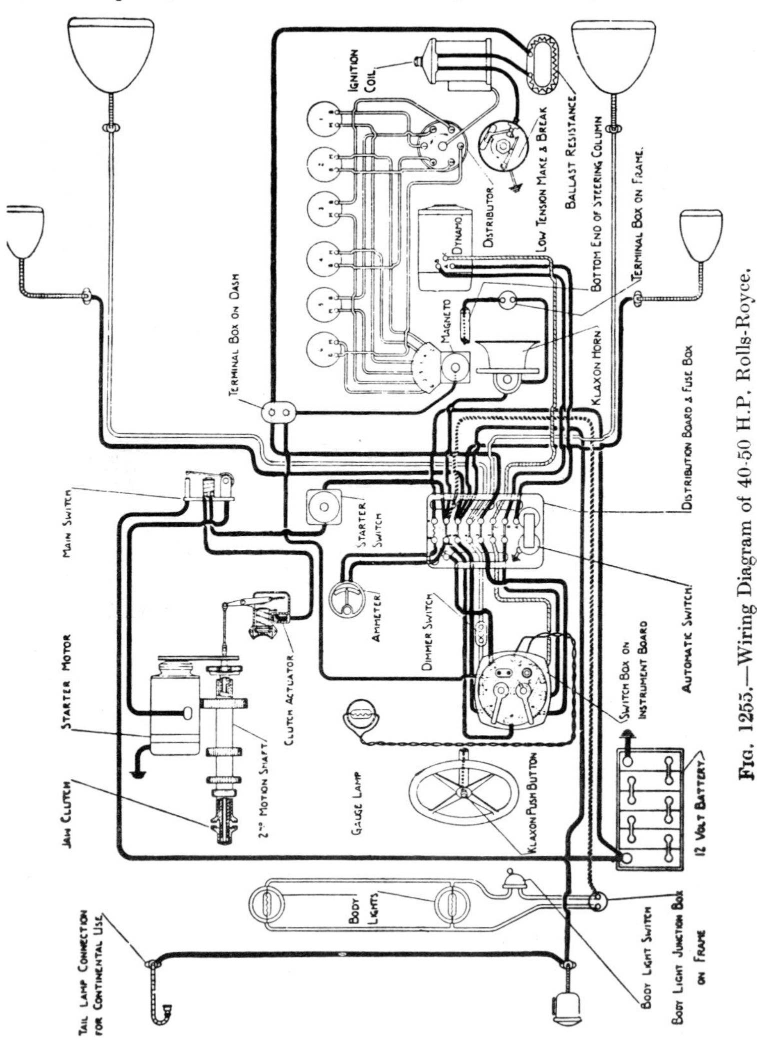

Fig. 1255.—Wiring Diagram of 40-50 H.P. Rolls-Royce.

After screwing ring G until ring G_1 makes contact with collar F, unscrew it only $\frac{3}{16}$ of a turn, *i.e.*, three holes, then with the floor boards removed, watch the clutch shaft and declutch with the engine idling. After noting the time the shaft takes to stop, increase the clearance by one hole on ring G, and again observe the time the shaft takes to stop. This operation may be repeated several times, and it will be found

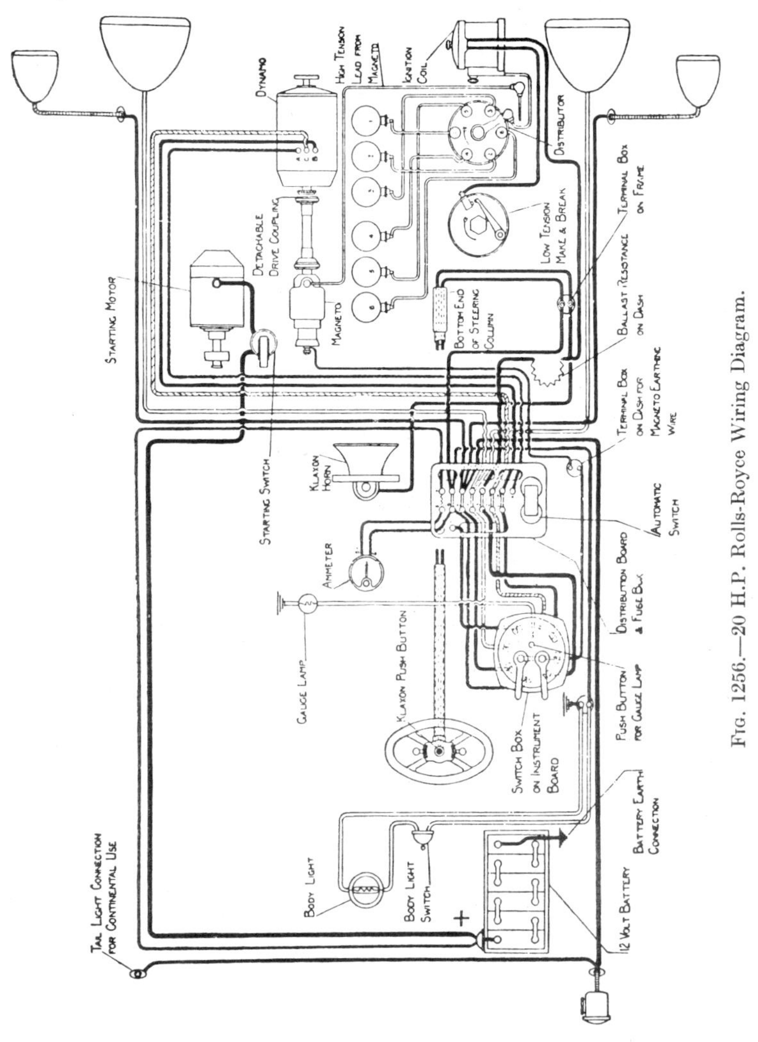

FIG. 1256.—20 H.P. Rolls-Royce Wiring Diagram.

that the period will decrease to a minimum with a certain setting, and then again increase. That setting should, therefore, be retained, which, after experiment, results in the clutch stopping in the shortest time. There is an oil hole in the clutch trunnion, so that a few drops of oil can be injected monthly,

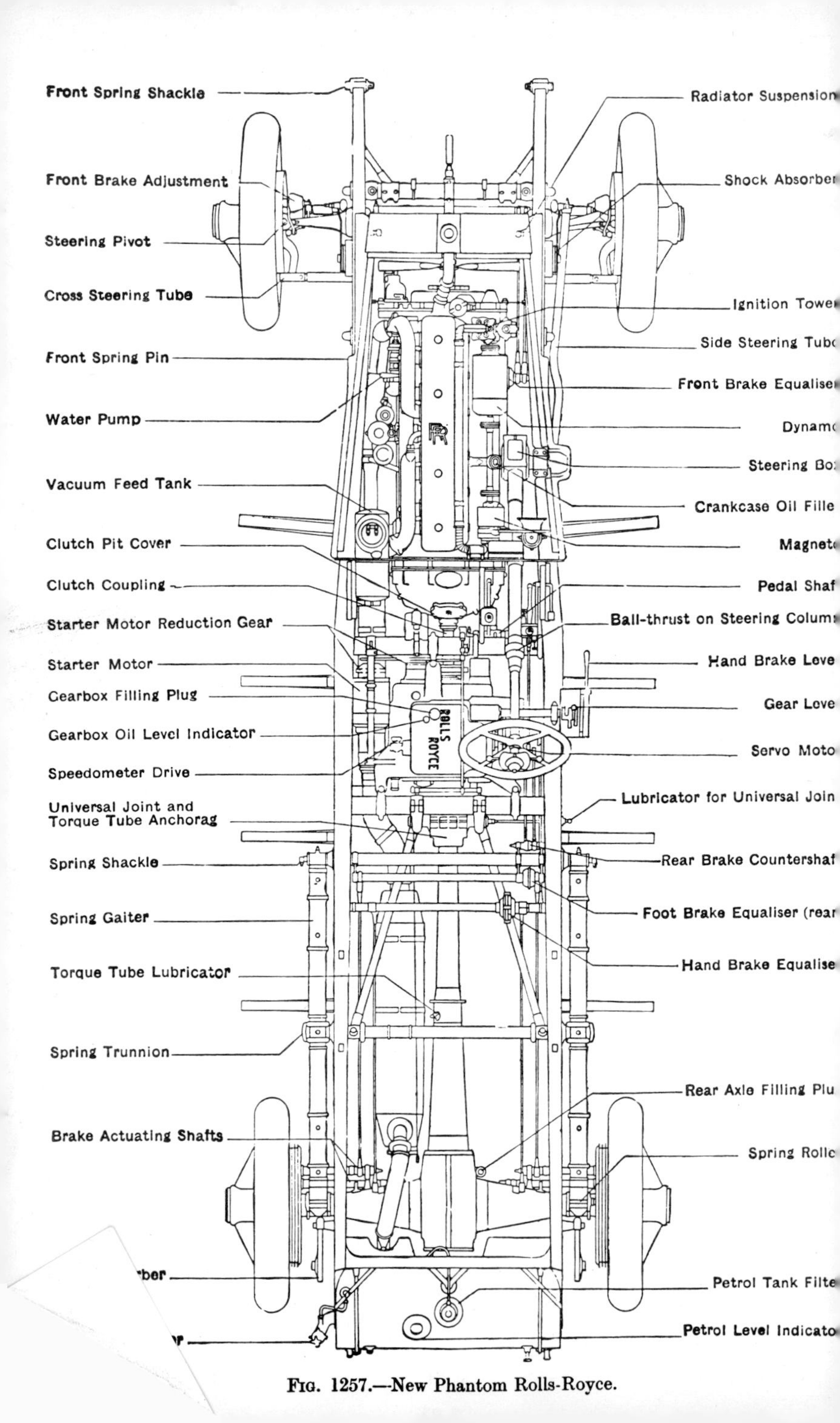

FIG. 1257.—New Phantom Rolls-Royce.

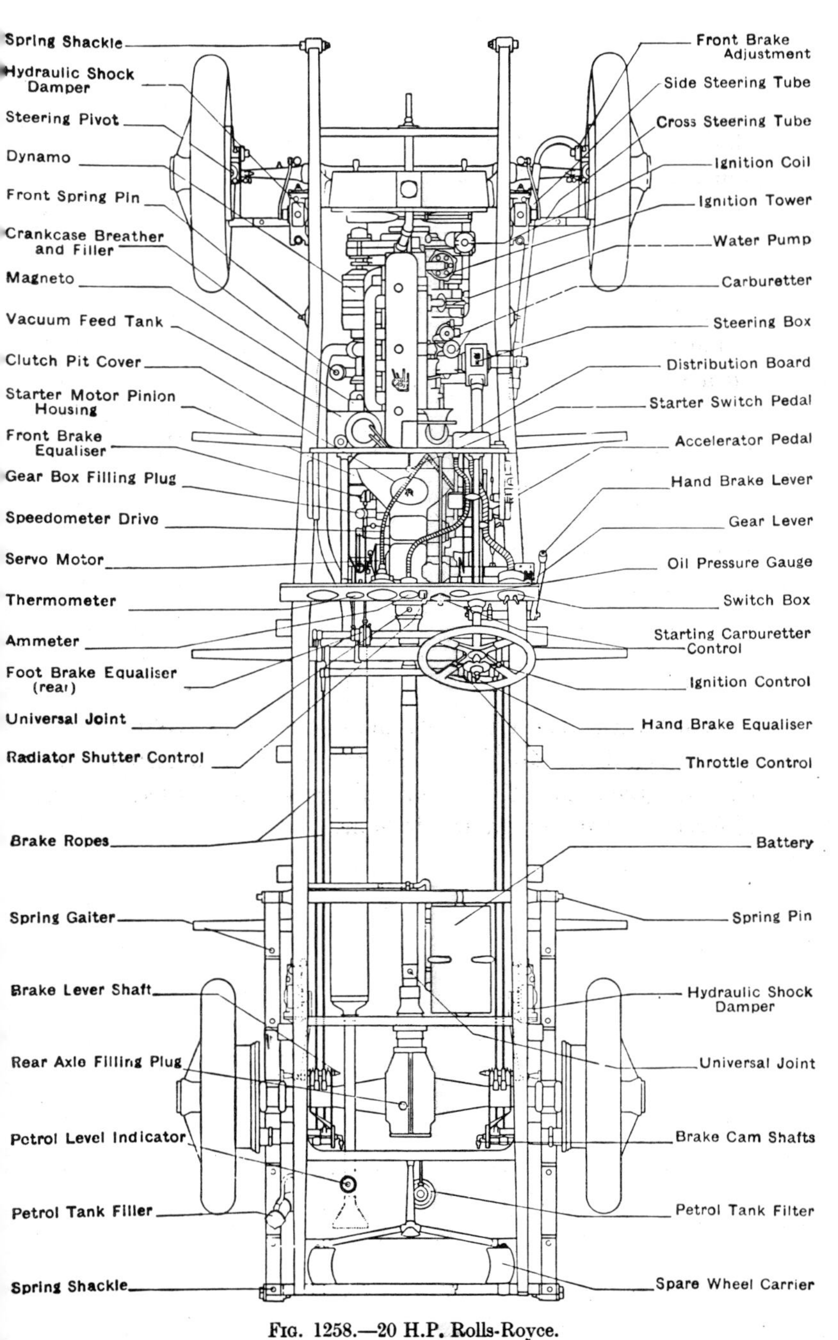

Fig. 1258.—20 H.P. Rolls-Royce.

or every 2,000 miles for the lubrication of the ball thrust bearing and the inner end of bearing of the clutch withdrawal shaft M. The bearing of the outer end of this shaft is lubricated by injecting oil into its open end M_1; at the same time the joints of levers J should be lubricated. Lubrication of the universal joint within the fly-wheel is effected by injecting into the hollow clutch shaft through hole M.

The back axle is really quite a simple straightforward job. A filler plug for oil is provided on its casing; it is arranged on a spout to ensure that the correct level is not exceeded.

A 12-volt wiring system, single pole with all negative leads earthed to the chassis frame, is fitted on Rolls-Royce chassis. The arrangement involves the use of three leads from the dynamo and distribution box, the actual leads being coloured as follows :—

Lead.	Colour.	Corresponding Letter on Dynamo.
Negative	Red and black	A
Positive	Black	B
Field	White and black	C

The wiring diagram shows the lay-out (Fig. 1256).

As regards the 20 H.P. Rolls-Royce, the plan view of the chassis given and the wiring diagram show what slight differences there are in the lay-out.

SUNBEAM

SIX AND EIGHT CYLINDER

There are four six-cylinder Sunbeam models and one eight-cylinder. The four six-cylinder types are respectively the 16 H.P., 20 H.P., 25 H.P. and the 3 litre; whilst the eight-cylinder is rated at 35 H.P. In their general features they do not differ very greatly. The 16 H.P. model has a bore of 67·5 mm. and a stroke of 95 mm. with tappet clearances with engine warm, inlet ·006 in. and exhaust ·008 in., or if checked when cold, inlet ·004 in. and exhaust ·006 in. The valve timing for this model is :—

Inlet opens	8° before T.D.C.
Inlet closes	62° after B.D.C.
Exhaust opens	49° before B.D.C.
Exhaust closes	11° after T.D.C.

The crank-case holds 14 pints of oil, and the standard radiator and water jacket 2·375 gals. (Colonial model 3 gals.) of water, while 12 gals. are contained in the petrol tank. The piston clearances are 4 mm. at top and they are sealed by four rings. On this model M-L coil ignition is fitted with a hand advance of 15° and an automatic advance on the distributor of 15°, making the total ignition advance 30°. The contact point gaps are ·012 to ·015 in., and the order of firing of the cylinders is 1, 5, 3, 6, 2, 4. A Claudel-Hobson V.36A carburettor is fitted, and the lighting is provided by a 12-volt battery of 66 amp.-hours' capacity. The dynamo charging rate is 10 amps.

There is no pedal adjustment for the clutch, which has a free movement of $\frac{1}{4}$ to $\frac{1}{2}$ in. minimum to maximum. The clutch adjustment is by a screwed jaw between the clutch pedal and clutch lever. The oil pressure when the engine is idling should show about 5 lbs. on the gauge, but when the car is running about 30 miles an hour after the engine is warm, the pressure rises to 20 lbs. per square inch, and this oil pressure applies to all Sunbeam cars.

Both the 20 H.P. Sunbeam and the 3-litre model have six-cylinder engines with a bore of 75 mm. and a stroke of 110 mm., with tappet clearances ·006 in. and ·008 in. for inlet and exhaust respectively, with engine warm, similarly to the 16 H.P. model for the 20 H.P. The timing of the 20 H.P. model, however, is different from that of the 3-litre, as under :—

	3-Litre.	20 H.P.
Inlet opens	8°	5 to 6° before T.D.C.
Inlet closes	46°	61° after B.D.C.
Exhaust opens . . .	46°	49·5° before B.D.C.
Exhaust closes . . .	14°	9·6° after T.D.C.

The tappet clearances for the 3-litre when engine is warm are, inlet ·010 in., exhaust ·015 in., or if checked cold, inlet ·008 in. and exhaust ·013 in. The crank-case oil capacity is 11 pints and the radiator 2·6 gals. for the 20 H.P. standard model and 3 gals. for the Colonial model, combined with a 12-gal. petrol tank carried in the rear. The piston clearance is the same for all the Sunbeam cars. The 20 H.P. is fitted with magneto B.T.H. model CE.6, with hand advance of 15° and an automatic advance of 25°, making a total of 40°. The order of firing of the cylinders is 1, 5, 3, 6, 2, 4. A Claudel-Hobson V.36B carburettor is fitted. The electrical system is similar and of the same capacity as the 16 H.P. 12 volts 16 amp.-hours.

Internal expanding four wheel brakes are fitted, vacuum servo operated, having one main adjustment and also separate adjustments for each of the six brakes.

The 3-litre model has a dry sump and so is provided with a tank with a capacity of 5 gals. of oil, which the pump circulates under pressure to the various bearings, etc. The radiator contains 2·9 gals. and the petrol tank 18 gals. A B.T.H. CE.6 magneto is fitted with a hand advance of 15°. Two Claudel-Hobson H.42A carburettors are fitted, and while the lighting is on the 12-volt system, the battery has a 90 amp.-hour capacity, though the dynamo charging rate is 10 amps. as on other Sunbeam cars.

The 25 H.P. Sunbeam has its six cylinders with a bore of 80 mm. and a stroke of 120 mm., with tappet clearances as for the 20 H.P., as also is the timing of the valves. The crank-case holds 15 pints of oil, radiator 4 gals., and Colonial 4·3 gals. of water, and the rear petrol tank 16 gals. The magneto is the same as the 20 H.P. with the same advance. So also is the order of firing of the cylinders, but the carburettor is an AZP.1. This car also has vacuum servo operated four wheel brakes.

The eight-cylinder Sunbeam, rated at 35 H.P., has its cylinder bore of 85 mm. and stroke of 120 mm. The tappet clearances with the engine warm are ·006 in. and exhaust ·008 in., while the valve timing is as follows :—

Inlet opens	3° before T.D.C.
Inlet closes	48° after B.D.C.
Exhaust opens	43° before B.D.C.
Exhaust closes	14° after T.D.C.

The piston clearance is 2 mm. at the top, and four rings are fitted on each piston. A B.T.H. CE.8 box-type magneto is fitted with 15° hand advance and 25° automatic advance, making 40° total advance. The contact point gaps are ·012 to ·015 in., and the order of firing of the cylinders is 1, 3, 7, 4, 8, 6, 2, 5. A Claudel-Hobson M.N.Z. carburettor is fitted on this Sunbeam and a 12-volt Rotax lighting equipment of 75 amp.-hours.

The following are the Claudel Hobson carburettor settings for the undermentioned models :—

Car.	Carb.	Choke.	Pilot.	Main.	Power.
16 H.P.	V.36 A	30	75	210	70
20 H.P.	V.36 B	27	130	270	80
25 H.P.	AZP	29	80	290	70

A central system of chassis lubrication, as fitted to the 20 H.P. six-cylinder Sunbeam, is shown in the illustration (Fig. 1326). By this system a spring-loaded plunger pump,

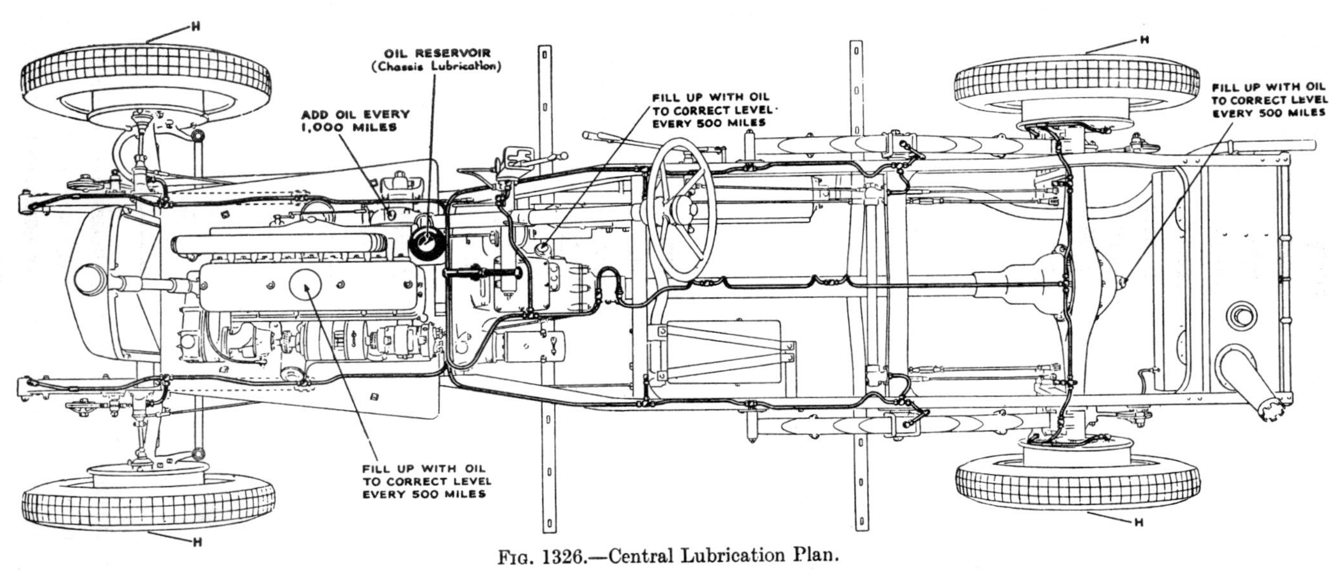

FIG. 1326.—Central Lubrication Plan.

operated by the foot, is situated to the left of the clutch pedal. When the plunger is depressed and held down for a period of four or five seconds, oil flows from the reservoir, mounted on the engine side of the dashboard, through a non-return valve, and fills the pump chamber. On removing the foot, the spring slowly returns the plunger to its normal position and ejects a charge of oil just taken in, which is forced out of the pump into the five pipe lines connected to it, and thence to the feed plugs or valves fitted on the various points requiring lubrication. These valves are so regulated that they pass the exact quantity of oil required by the particular bearings. To prevent jet stoppage the oil

FIG. 1327.—Showing Main Adjusting Nut for Four Wheel Brakes.

is filtered at the tank filler by a filter insert. There is another filter at the tank outlet, and each connection is fitted with a small pad of filtering material. The plunger must always be depressed to its fullest extent, as the pump itself is divided into five separate compartments, each one connected to a different pipe line.

Lubrication of parts on the front axle and front brake gear, as well as steering gear, is not effected through this system, but by means of the oil gun through the usual lubricators. The steering box, gear-box, and back axle gears are also not lubricated from the central system, but through the oil plugs provided for these respective units.

Sunbeam brakes are on all four wheels of the chassis and are applied by pressure on the brake pedal operated through Dewandre vacuum servo. The joints of the air pipe between the vacuum servo and the induction pipe of the engine must be kept tight, as in the event of an air leak developing, both the efficiency of the servo and the running of the engine will be affected. When any adjustment to the brakes becomes necessary, it will be found that there is an individual adjustment provided for each of the four wheel brakes, but the main adjustment is effected by the nut A (see Fig. 1327). Independent adjustment of the front wheel brakes is effected by means of the adjusting nuts F and B (see Fig. 1328) and by the nuts A and B for the rear wheel brakes (see Fig. 1329). The nuts marked A are the adjustments for the hand brake, and the nuts B for the rear brake operated from the pedal.

FIG. 1328.—Showing Near-Side Front Wheel.

F, B, Brake adjusting nuts.
A, Eccentric or equalising stop.
L, Lubricators.

Regular lubrication is most important.

If the balance of adjustment between all four brakes has been disturbed by the removal of the brake shoes, rods, etc., it can be restored as follows: The lock-nut A (see Fig. 1327) should be unscrewed for several turns, the car should then be jacked up from underneath each axle, so that the weight is on the springs and all the wheels are off the ground. The front brakes should now be adjusted through their independent adjustments until both sets of front brake shoes are just touching the drums. The rear wheel brakes should also be adjusted by means of the nuts B (see Fig. 1329) until the shoes are just touching the drums in the same way as the front brake shoes. The main adjustment nut A (Fig. 1327) should then be screwed up to the required position. No separate lock-nut is provided for this, as it is a self-locking nut. When this has been done, both the front and rear wheel brakes should be further adjusted so that the shoes are just free of the drums. As a final test, apply pressure to the pedal when the front and rear wheel brakes should all come into operation equally at the same time. This should be

Fig. 1329.—Showing Brake Rods and Adjusting Nuts to Rear Wheel Brakes.

A, Hand brake adjusting nuts.
B, Foot brake adjusting nuts.

done with the wheels pulled round into full steering lock in each direction. In all cases care must be taken to see that the off-side and near-side brakes exert the same braking power when the pedal is depressed. For the front wheel brakes an eccentric stop marked A (Fig. 1328) is fitted to hold the front brake shoes in their proper position relative to the drum. When the shoe linings are worn, this stop must be adjusted by about one-eighth of a turn of the screw (the nut is a lock-nut), which is sufficient. The screw must be held firmly with the screw-driver both while unscrewing the lock-nut and also when tightening up again. After adjustment each front wheel should swing freely. If it does not, the adjustment has been overdone, and the screw will have to

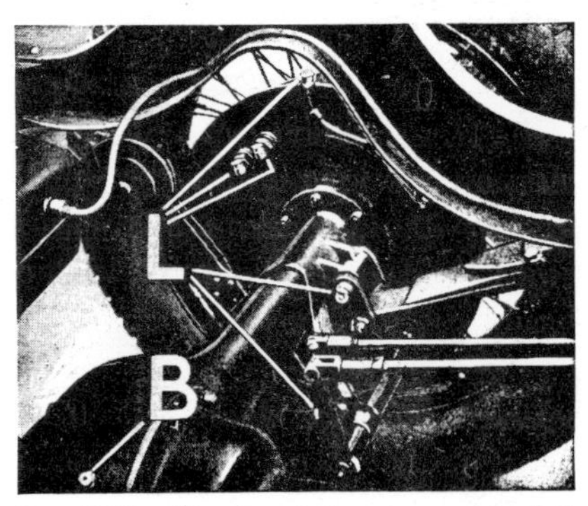

Fig. 1330.—Showing Lubricators marked L on rear wheel; B is not a lubricator but a breather for the differential casing.

be turned back slightly until the wheel does spin. This should be tested with the wheels swung round in full steering lock in each direction.

To remove the front hub and brake drum after taking off the wheel, unscrew the hub dust cap, remove the small pin and the nut on the end of the shaft inside, then the hub can be reached with a box-spanner. The front brake drums should always be removed with the hub as shown in Fig. 1331. If the front hub bearings should require adjustment, care must be taken to see that they are not screwed up too tightly. The inner nut should be screwed up until there remains two or three thousandths of an inch end play. After placing lock-washers in position and the outer nut screwed home, practically all this end play will then be taken up.

FIG. 1331.—Showing Front Wheel Brake with Wheel and Brake Drum Removed.

To remove the rear brake drums, unscrew the nuts which hold same on the hub; if the drum should be too tight to pull off after the nuts have been unscrewed, tap it lightly round its outer edge with a mallet. Do not use an ordinary metal hammer. There are six of these nuts marked A (see Fig. 1332) to be seen at the rear of the flange plate. If these are removed the hub and axle shaft may easily be withdrawn. To release the hubs from the axle, after these have been

FIG. 1332.—Unscrew Nuts A to Remove Hub.

withdrawn bodily, unscrew cover B and a castle nut and split pin will be seen. If these are removed, the hub can be

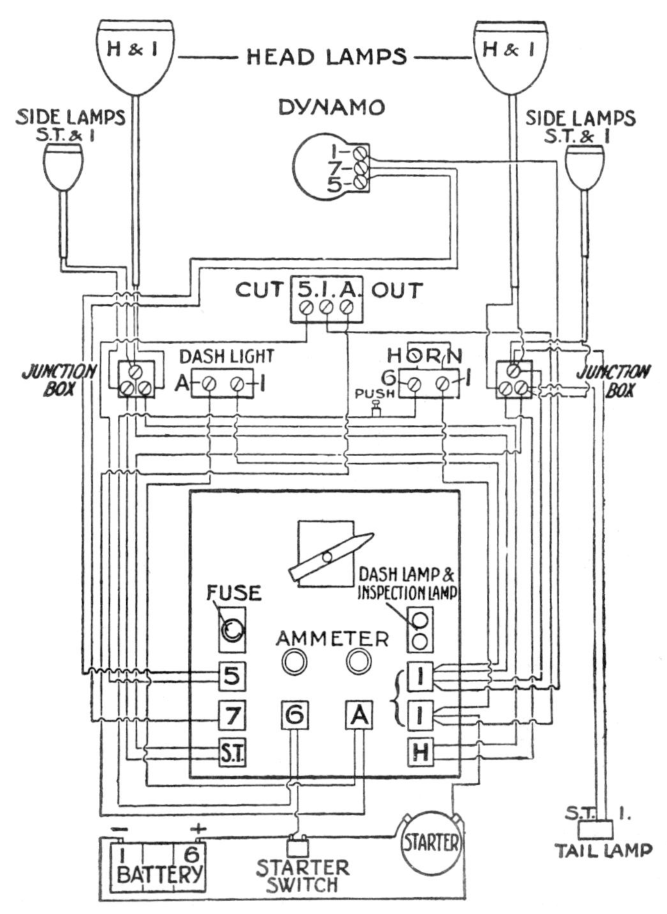

FIG 1333.—Wiring Diagram.

withdrawn from the axle shaft. When replacing the hub and shaft, the nuts A must be screwed up tightly, and to lubricate the hub remove cover B.

TROJAN

FOUR CYLINDER

The Trojan, formerly made by Leyland Motors Ltd. and now by Trojan Ltd., is one of the few chassis existing to-day fitted with a two-stroke engine instead of one working on the four-cycle principle. Therefore it has no valves, and as the oil is mixed with the petrol it lubricates the pistons and cylinders with the charge of gas, and is pump circulated through all the crankshaft bearings. The engine contains two distinct and separate crank-cases. The right-hand cylinders share a common combustion chamber, and the left-hand cylinders are similarly connected. The pistons act as a pump, and in receding from the crank-case they create therein a partial vacuum until the skirt of the lower piston uncovers the inlet port, which opens up communication between the carburettor and the crank-case. The space in the crank-case is thus filled with an explosive mixture drawn from the carburettor, which mixture on the return of the piston becomes compressed and is driven through the transfer port as it becomes uncovered by the head of the upper piston.

This compression in the crank-case and transfer of the new charge into the combustion chamber is effected in every complete revolution of the crank, that is in two strokes of the pistons. On the other side of the pistons, namely, the side remote from the crank-case, the processes of charging, compression, explosion, and exhaust are effected. The mixture is fired every two strokes of the piston. The first stroke is charging and compressing, and the second stroke exploding and exhausting. The illustration is self-explanatory, showing the cycle of operations.

Engines with the letters XL before the engine number have a cubic capacity of 1,488 c.c. instead of 1,527 c.c. The four cylinders have a bore of $2\frac{1}{2}$ in. and a stroke of $4\frac{5}{8}$ in., and the piston clearances are ·005 in. and three rings are included. Remy coil ignition is used which has 18° automatic advance. The contact points gap is ·015 in. The cylinders are coupled in pairs so that they fire in the order of 1, 2. A special Trojan Amac carburettor is incorporated with a hand-controlled variable jet. The lighting system is on the 6-volt system with a battery capacity of 40 to 80 amp.-hours and dynamo charging rate of 8 to 10 amps.

Should an engine not start, one of four things is defective, the compression, air-petrol ratio, spark, or timing. As the compression and timing can scarcely become defective with a Trojan engine, the trouble is either the spark or the mixture. If a high-tension wire is detached from a plug, then the length of the spark from this to the "earth" should be at least $\frac{1}{4}$ in. when engine is being cranked by hand. If this is in order, then the Champion plugs should be removed to see if points are not more than ·015 in. apart.

If the ignition is in order, the mixture is wrong, and—except when starting from cold—the mixture is generally too rich, due to running of engine on rich mixture prior to stopping. The excess petrol must be pumped out while mixture lever is set at zero.

To avoid recurrence of this trouble, the mixture lever must be kept on the low side and the throttle set so as not to let the engine run too slowly when idling.

The above precautions, coupled with the latest type of primer pump, attached to carburettor and operated from instrument board, should eliminate starting troubles.

All cars delivered after 11th December 1925 have their petrol tanks fitted with an oil mixing baffle. Tanks so fitted are marked with the letter B on the left end.

An epicyclic gear-box is installed in the Trojan. If it is necessary to remove this from the car, proceed as follows :—

(1) Detach the fourteen flexible coupling springs by first

SECTION THROUGH AA.

Fig. 2, I. Carburetted air entering vacuous crank-case.

iv. Compression complete, spark explodes the charge.

Fig. 3. II. Compressed explosive mixture in crank-case about to enter cylinder through transfer port.

v. Explosion complete, burnt gases escaping through exhaust port. The new charge is about to enter and take the place of the burnt gases.

Fig. 4. III. Transfer from crank-case to cylinders complete, and compression in cylinders about to commence.

vi. III. Repeats.

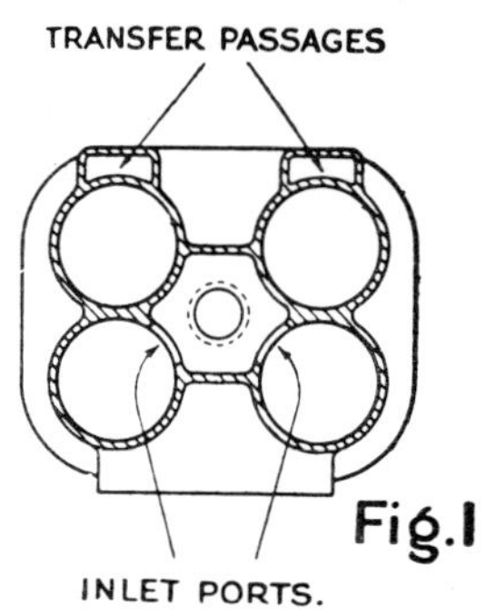

FIG. 1368.

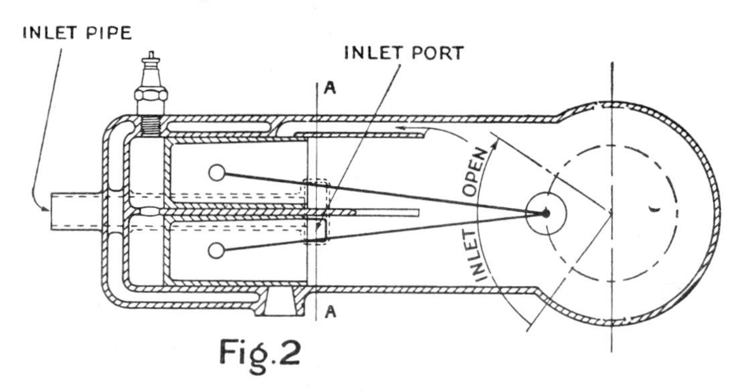

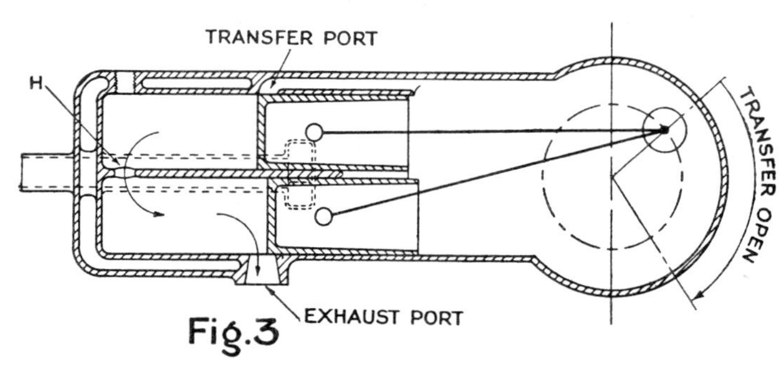

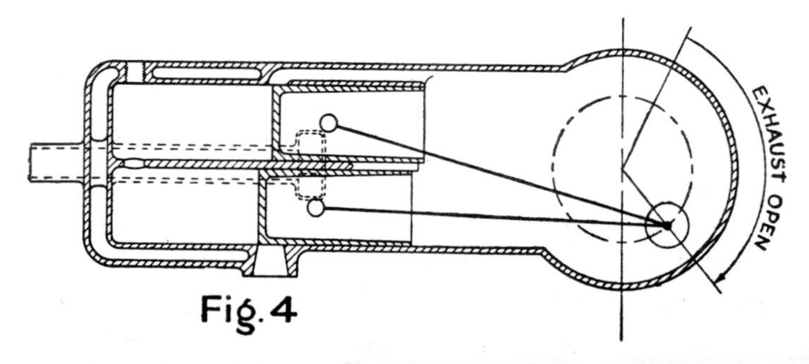

FIG. 1369.

removing the fourteen outside screws. Place a piece of plain rod in each empty hole whilst each inside screw is being

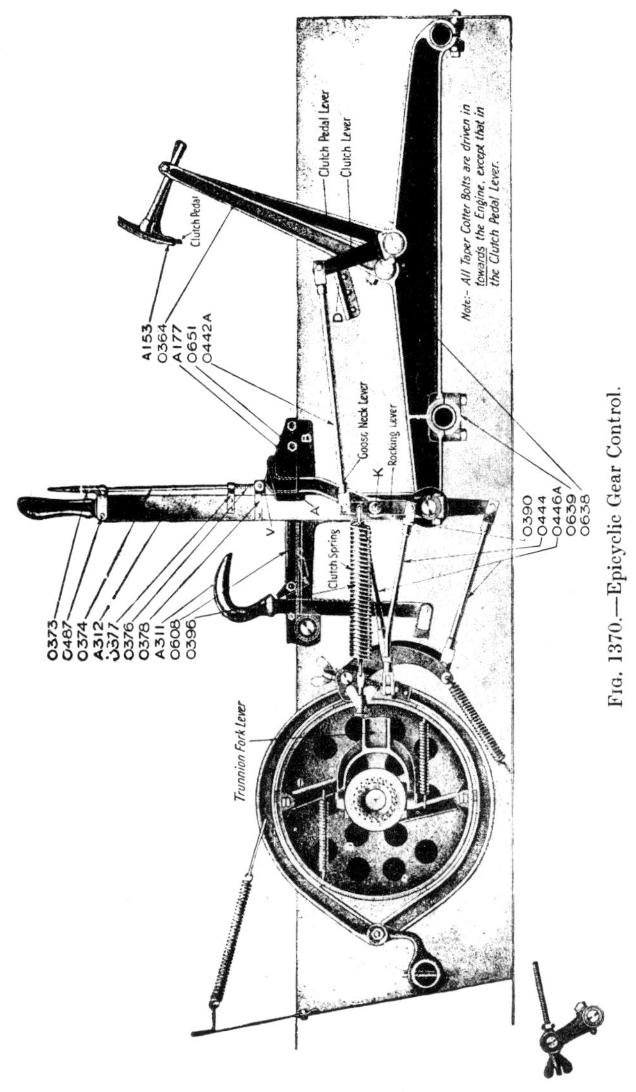

Fig. 1370.—Epicyclic Gear Control.

removed. (2) Loosen the screw in the locating collar about six complete turns until the collar will move round on the shaft. (3) Remove the low-speed and reverse rods 0446A and the low-gear pull-off spring underneath the low-speed drum (Fig. 1370). (4) Release the anchor shaft by taking out the screws from each end. The anchor shaft can be prevented from rotating by inserting a tommy bar in the centre of the shaft. (5) Remove the small chain sprocket, with the aid of the withdrawing screw, or with a service tool, and with the same screw remove the transmission brake drum and also the plate. (6) Withdraw the shaft with the special tool provided, or lever it out with jemmies or pinch bars. The gear-box can now be lifted out. If only the gear shaft needs removing, items (2) and (6) alone are necessary. Care must be taken, however, if the gear shaft has seized in the low-speed drum bearing. When the shaft is being withdrawn the drum must be kept back,

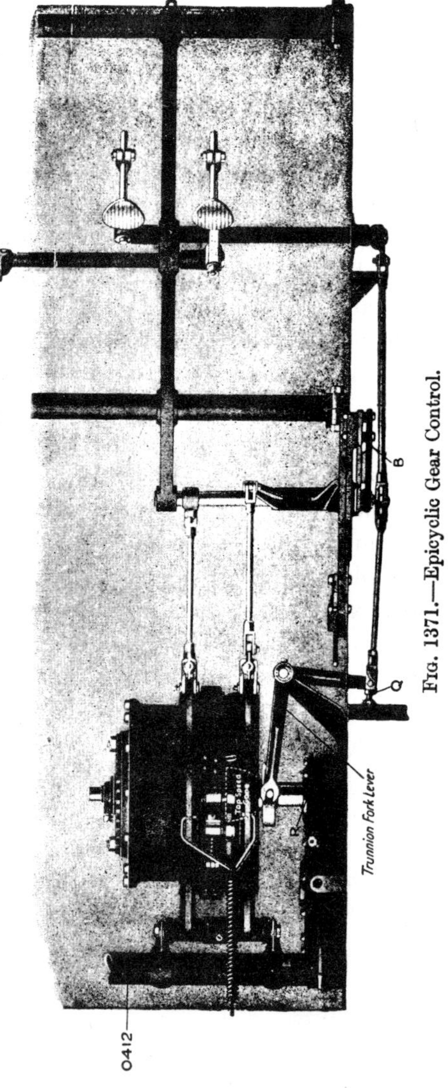

Fig. 1371.—Epicyclic Gear Control.

and, in the absence of the special service tool, packing must be arranged between the drum and the reduction gear-box at points where the fragile aluminium cover is supported. If the shaft is too badly seized to come right through the top-speed cone, draw it as far as possible, then remove the engine and epicyclic gear-box, knock back cone, and file high places off the shaft. It may still be possible to use the shaft again if it is carefully cleaned up to be a free fit in the low-speed drum sleeve.

In the erection of the epicyclic gear-box in the car, assembling must be made of the parts in the reverse order of dismantling, making sure that none of the parts detailed in the dissembling has been omitted. When securing the locating collar with the screw there may be some doubt as to whether the point of the screw has entered the hole in the shaft. To ascertain this, first screw up lightly in the wrong place, release the screw half a turn, then—when it is in the right place—the screw can be screwed in several turns.

In assembling the epicyclic gear-box the bushes should be pressed inside the gear-box, the reverse drum hub and gear-box cover. Then reamer out until they are a very free running fit to the respective parts on which they run. Assemble the planet spindles and the hardened washers in gear-box, insert spindle locating pegs, secure the nuts with locking plates, assemble the reverse drum hub and drum complete in the gear-box, and press the 26-toothed gear wheel into position, then place the washer and the 20-toothed gear wheel in such a position that the oil holes in the gear wheel correspond with the holes in the slow-speed drum. (For removing gear wheels use service tool No. 373.)

If the keep ring will not go into position the rounded edges of the bushes may have to be scraped to enable the slow speed drum to go further in. Press the bushes into planet gear groups, reamer until they are very free running on their spindles. With $\frac{1}{8}$-in. drill follow through the hole already drilled in each of the smallest planet gear wheels and insert the $\frac{3}{32}$-in. diameter peg until it projects $\frac{3}{64}$ in. inside the bush. Caulk the steel over the head of this peg to ensure that it cannot work back. The two planet groups of gears can now be slid into position; the two groups must slide simultaneously, otherwise the correct meshing of the gears necessary to ensure an even distribution of the drive will not be obtained.

The advantage of this pin-and-groove system of assembling will be appreciated by those who have spent hours trying to assemble similar epicyclic planets. If one planet group has been assembled wrongly it may be impossible to get the other one in at all, or, worse still, it may be assembled so that it drives against the other instead of sharing the drive.

Insert the other two hardened washers and apply gold size or coach varnish to the joint on gear-box and cover. Insert the inner ring for spring drive and the nut locking plates, tighten the nuts and then the peripheral screws. Inset shaft and keep collar. Rotate the shaft to ascertain that the gears are all free endwise. Introduce about ½ pint of engine oil through the oil plug hole.

The following is the method for fitting new low speed or reverse band on the epicyclic gear. Remove transmission band anchor shaft (the attachment to the chassis behind the gear-box) by undoing the set-screws at each end. Bring the anchor shaft to the top, and insert the new band under the keep rings on the anchor shaft. Replace the anchor shaft in position temporarily by replacing the screws previously mentioned, and see if the new relined band fits the drum properly. If the lining does not conform to the curvature of the drum, the band must be removed and bent on the bench with a wooden mallet until the desired fit is obtained. If anything, the lining should make contact on the drum at the heel end first, rather than the toe. The anchor shaft can now be replaced and the set-screws done up tightly, and the curved lever pins in front of the gear-box inserted.

For fitting a new top speed band after relining, it is essential to shape the band carefully to suit the drums, otherwise the gears will be noisy in neutral; the bands will heat up and will not grip properly when travelling in top. The clutch stop Q (Figs. 1370 and 1371) is provided to prevent the top speed cone from being forced against the low speed drum by the clutch spring, thus producing wear, noise, and end thrust on the ball bearing. The stop should be adjusted so that a thin card just fails to be nipped behind the top speed cone. The stop in the other direction is the reduction gear-box cover R, and it is most important that the top speed band should not be adjusted too tightly to prevent this stop from being reached. The length of the clutch fork rod is adjustable to enable the stops B and R to be encountered at the same time. One of the bands is painted white, to guard against one band being adjusted twice and the other being missed.

For shortening the chain, release the eight spring chair bolts, pull the top of the right-hand wheel forward with a

FIG. 1372.—Chain Adjustment.

sudden jerk to slacken the chain, push out any one rivet with the special rivet removing clamp, then push out the rivet next but one to it, thus removing a complete or double link equal to $1\frac{1}{2}$ in. chain, join up the chain with a new rivet and caulk its end. In the absence of the special rivet removing clamp it will be necessary in order to push out the rivets to remove the chain and take it to the bench. Replace the chain over the sprockets and tighten roughly by rotating the back wheel suddenly backwards, then adjust with the chain adjuster. It is not feasible to shorten the chain in this manner more than twice, because after a third shortening it would become out of pitch with the sprockets and would persist in jumping the teeth. When it becomes necessary to fit a new chain the sprockets or chain wheels should also be renewed, as it is false economy to run a new chain on worn sprockets.

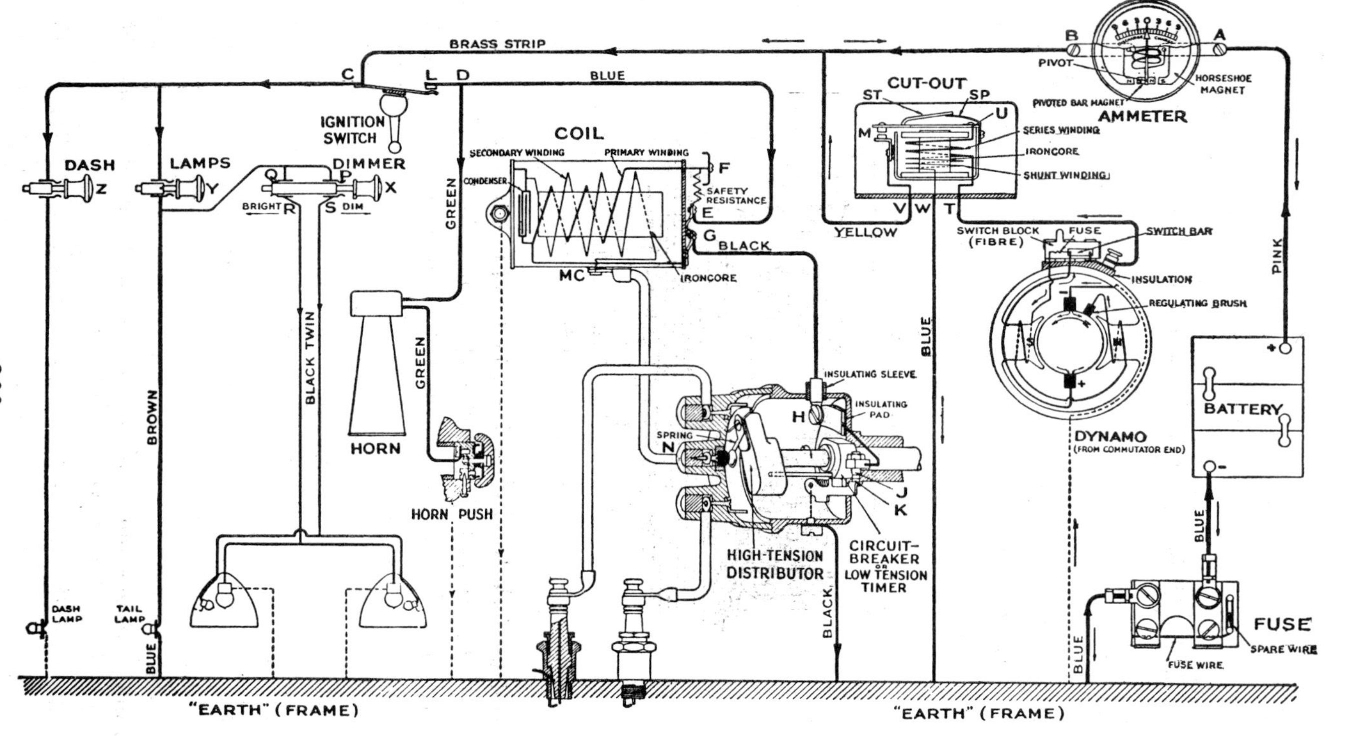

FIG. 1373.—Wiring Diagram.

VAUXHALL

SIX CYLINDER

In these days of multi-model manufacturers, it is quite out of the ordinary to come across a firm standardising on one model, but Vauxhall Motors Ltd., of Luton, at present produce no other but their well-tried six-cylinder 20-60 H.P. overhead valved engine car. This has a bore and stroke of 75 × 110 mm. with a capacity of 2,910 c.c., and is rated at 20·9 H.P. Its six cylinders are cast monobloc, integral with the crank-case. The overhead valves are operated by enclosed push-rods, and the lubrication is provided under pressure by a submerged gear pump which is driven from centre of camshaft, and is fitted with oil strainer. Impeller circulation and fan cooling are provided and an enclosed dry plate clutch. Four forward speeds and a reverse are given in the gear-box, and the propeller shaft is of the open tubular type with fabric coupling front and rear. The rear axle is of the one-piece banjo type casing, spiral bevel gears, semi-floating. Marles patent cam and roller steering is incorporated.

The crank-case holds about 2¼ gals. of oil, the radiator and cooling connections 4½ gals. of water, and the petrol tank 14 gals.

The cylinder head can be dismantled in the usual way, and the valves may be removed and seats checked by using the valve compressor supplied in the tool kit, depressing the valve springs, and removing the split cones from the recesses in valve stems. Always check valve seatings when regrinding. Should it, however, be necessary to remove a valve spring without disturbing the head, the valve may be held up by means of a bent rod inserted through the plug hole during the process of spring removal and in refitting the springs. When attending to one or more valve springs, there is no need to place the piston in question at T.D.C., because the valve cannot fall through into the cylinder, as it will rest on top of the cylinder block. When resting in this position the valve stem still protrudes through its guide. When resetting the valve clearances, remove the valve rocker cover and run the engine until it is thoroughly warmed up. Close the throttle and retard the ignition. The engine will then be running as slowly as possible. Clearance is provided in the valve end of the rocker. The tappet clearance with the engine warm is ·0075 in. for both inlet and exhaust. The valve timing for this engine is :—

Inlet opens	At T.D.C.
Inlet closes	57° after B.D.C.
Exhaust opens	62° before B.D.C.
Exhaust closes	25° after T.D.C.

and the order of firing of the cylinders is 1, 5, 3, 6, 2, 4. Delco-Remy coil ignition, 12 volts, is provided, with 25° hand advance and 12° 16′ automatic, making the total maximum ignition advance 37° 16′.

Both crankshaft and camshaft pinions are marked by means of chisel cuts, and if these marks are in line and adjacent, the valves will be correctly timed.

If it has been necessary to remove the distributor, or if the ignition timing has been disturbed, it should be reset in the following manner : Turn the engine over by hand until the scribed line on the fly-wheel marked T.D.C. is seen through the inspection hole in the near-side of the fly-wheel housing (see Fig. 1374). The fly-wheel T.D.C. mark must then be brought in line with the centre of the inspection hole. Put the ignition control lever in the fully retarded position, and slacken the distributor clamping bolt. The body of the distributor should then be turned to that position in which the contacts (A, Fig. 1374) are on the point of opening when the engine is turned in the correct direction of rotation. If it is then found that the high-tension leads are not conveniently placed, it will be necessary to remove the distributor from the housing, rotate the shaft, and replace with the gear meshing in such a way as to bring the leads into a convenient position. The distributor clamping bolt should then be securely locked into position. A great deal of trouble

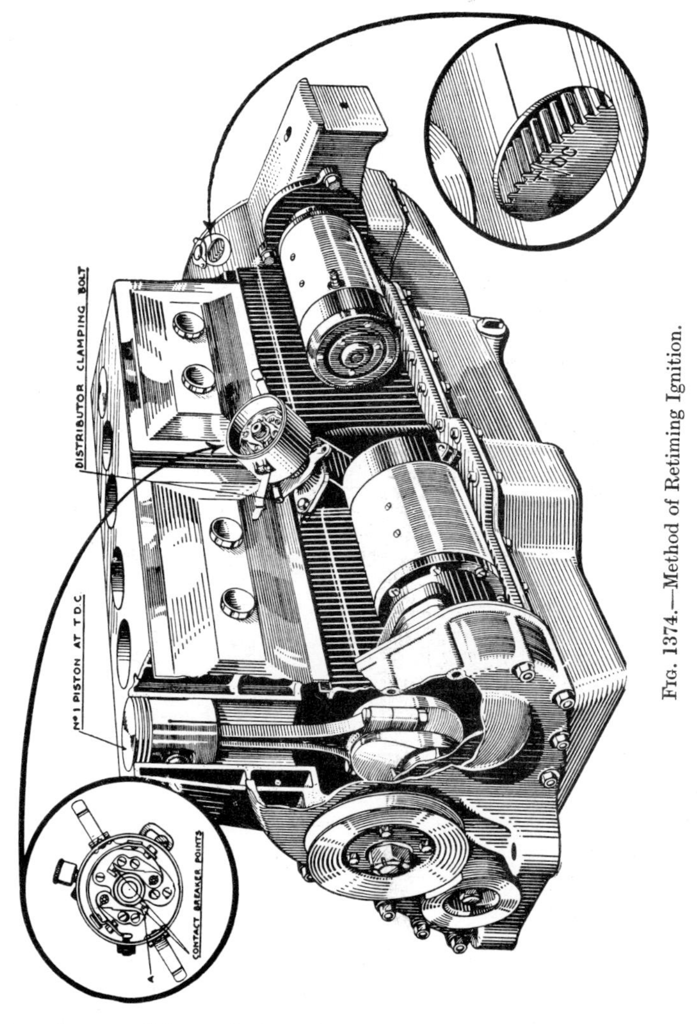

Fig. 1374.—Method of Retiming Ignition.

may be saved in retiming the ignition if care is taken to see that the engine is not turned over while the distributor is out of position. There will then be no difficulty in getting the gear to mesh correctly. The distributor should be so arranged that when the moulded cap is replaced the metal segment of the rotor is opposite the correct insert in the cap. The numbers of the leads are clearly moulded on the top of this cap. The correct contact points gap is ·020 in.

To dismantle and remove tappets, detach rocker cover, remove tappet coverplates, and depress rockers to allow removal of the push-rods and balls. The tappets, which operate in two guide blocks, six to each block, are readily removable by taking out the three screws which attach each block to the crank-case. Careful markings should be made

Fig. 1375.—Method of Adjusting Timing Chain.

during removal to ensure that the push-rods are returned to the positions from which they were originally taken.

To take up any stretch in the timing chain, loosen the nuts A (Fig. 1375) attaching the dynamo bearing housing to the timing gear-case, and turn the whole dynamo in an anti-clockwise direction, viewing from the rear, about the axis of the bottom retaining bolt.

The nut on the bottom bolt is somewhat inaccessible, but the dynamo drive housing can be turned sufficiently by inserting a short lever between the slotted flange and the crank-case after the two upper nuts have been slackened.

Do not exert any pressure on the dynamo body itself. The nuts may then be tightened and the engine temporarily run to ascertain whether the desired result of lessened noise has been attained. If not, the degree of tension must be increased or lessened, as circumstances dictate. It must be remembered that chains commonly stretch somewhat unevenly, so that if the tension is being judged by inspection and touch, it should be known before testing that the chain is in the tightest position it takes up during its travel.

Should there be any water leakage from the impeller gland, tighten the gland set-screws. If this adjustment does not check the leak, repack the gland, using special gland packing.

Should adjustment of the fan belt be necessary, remove the four bolts clamping together the flanges of the lower pulley, and replace the disc distance piece by one of thinner section. This distance piece is fitted between the flanges. A ball bearing fitted in the front end of the water pump body forms the fan bearing, and is located in position by a screwed retaining ring. The only attention to this is to supply grease through a grease gun nipple provided on the side of the pump body.

In regard to the single dry plate clutch, the outer ends of the levers operating on cam faces on the rear surface of pressure plate provide the clutch adjustment. Clutch adjustment is carried out by turning the clutch cover in a clockwise direction, thus bringing outer ends of levers into contact with the higher parts of the cam faces. This compensates for wear of the friction surfaces. Adjust the clutch at once in case of slip. Do not change pedal adjustment instead of adjusting the clutch. This latter component is accessible by removing floor board and hand-hole plate in clutch housing. Measure distance from the face of the clutch cover to the rear face of the release sleeve N in Fig. 1376, which should be $2\frac{11}{32}$ in. A gauge made of wire with wire of $2\frac{13}{32}$ in. bend at one end may be used to advantage. If this space is more than $2\frac{13}{32}$ in., loosen the six bolts M and turn the clutch coverplate a little more to the right. If less than $2\frac{13}{32}$ in., turn cover a little to the left. After correct setting has been obtained, tighten holding bolts. This completes the clutch adjustment.

To adjust the clutch pedal, press the latter down and note distance which the release sleeve travels. It should be pushed towards the fly-wheel $\frac{13}{32}$ in., which is necessary for a clean release. If it does not travel that distance, shift the pedal up a little by means of the slotted clutch pedal adjustment. There should be approximately 1 in. of pedal movement before release commences.

Fig. 1376.—Clutch.

The clutch pedal adjustment has now been set in its correct position and should not be touched again, because adjusting the clutch automatically brings the pedal back to the floor board.

A Claudel-Hobson carburettor is fitted to the Vauxhall, and the best setting is stated to be as follows :—

Power jet	120
Main jet	190
Pilot jet	90
Choke	26 mm.

The only trouble likely to be experienced will be due to grit under the needle valve, which can be removed by dismantling the petrol pipe union nut under the float chamber, removing the seating and washing this out with petrol. In the event of it being necessary to remove the needle valve, the screw A (Fig. 1377) in the side of the float chamber should be withdrawn, when the valve will fall out of the bottom of the

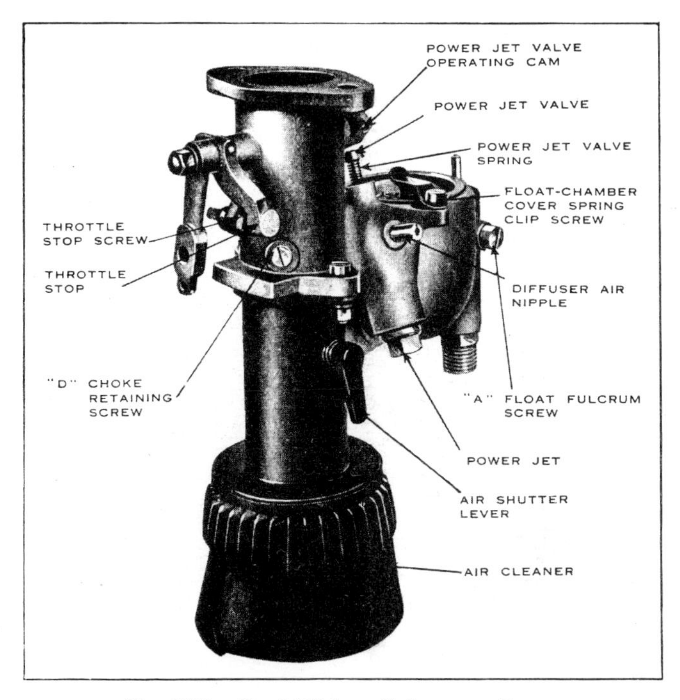

Fig. 1377.—Claudel-Hobson Carburettor—Front.

float chamber. Care should be taken to replace the float the same way up, also to ensure the float lever is in the collar of the needle valve before replacing seating.

Main Jet.—On no account should the hole in the jet be tampered with, or cleaned out with any form of metal wire. Foreign matter should be removed by blowing through the hole from the top of the jet, viz., in the reverse direction to the petrol flow.

Power Jet.—The power jet is operated by a cam fitted on

the end of the throttle spindle. This is set so that it begins to operate the power jet valve when the throttle is approximately half open. The power jet should be cleaned in the same manner as the main jet.

Slow-Running Jet.—The slow-running jet is removed by unscrewing the plug above the diffuser, and also the jet tube from the plug. Cleaning out should be the same as above.

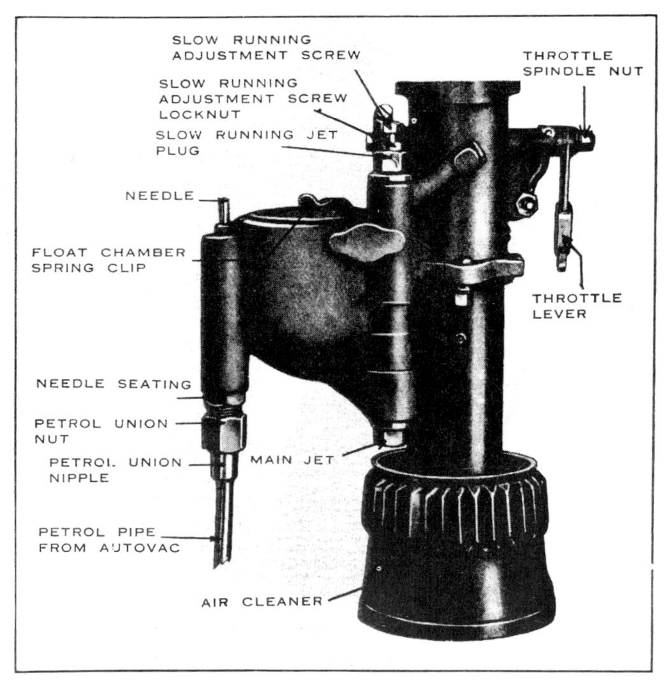

Fig. 1378.—Claudel-Hobson Carburettor—Rear.

When replacing, care should be taken that the washers are positioned correctly on the spigot of the jets.

Choke Tube.—To remove the choke tube, detach the air cleaner by removing the two small bolts holding it to the air intake pipe of the carburettor. Remove the screw D (Fig. 1377) which locates the position of the choke, and this can then be taken out. It is most important when replacing to make sure that the choke tube is the right way up (number at base), and that the small countersink registers with the hole for the choke screw.

The air cleaner fitted to the carburettor requires no attention, as it automatically ejects the extracted foreign matter.

The internal expanding four wheel brakes have external

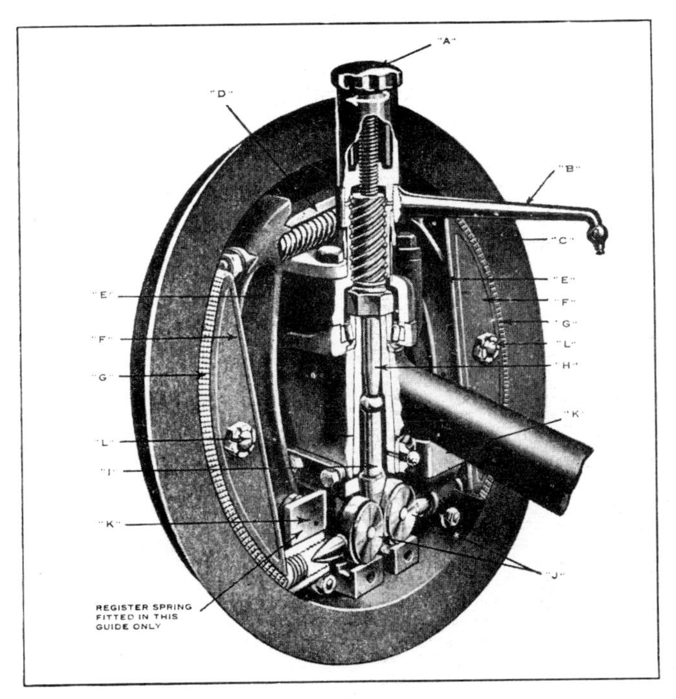

FIG. 1379.—Near-Side Front Brake looking from Rear of Axle.

A, Adjusting knob.
B, Brake actuating arm.
C, Brake drum.
D, Fulcrum bracket.
E, Brake shoe carrier.
F, Brake shoe.
G, Brake shoe liner.
H, Operating spindle.
I, Wedge-headed spindle.
J, Brake operating rollers.
K, Shoe carrier guides.
L, Brake shoe clamping bolt.

adjustment on each brake. When adjusting the brakes always attend to all four, because if the front brakes only are adjusted, there is a possibility of the rear failing to operate and the front brakes becoming dangerously powerful. Correctly adjusted, the braking is in the ratio of 1-3 on the front and 1 on the rear.

The front brake adjusting knob A (Fig. 1379) has a clockwise rotation for taking up wear, and the rear hand wheel (Fig. 1380) takes up wear by rotating in the direction of the pointers at the end of the spokes.

At intervals the brakes should be readjusted as follows :—

Jack up each wheel in turn and rotate the adjusting knob or hand wheel until the brake shoes rub, and then slacken off

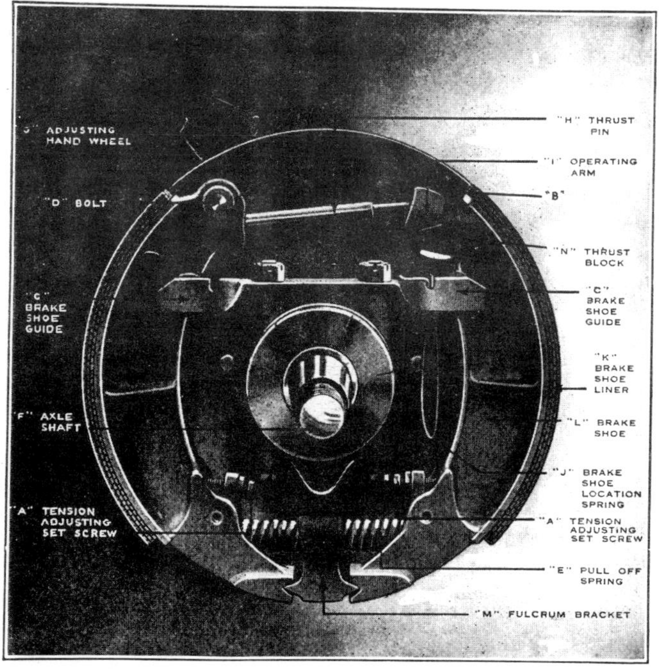

Fig. 1380.—Rear Brake.

the adjustment until the shoes are just clear. Although it is essential to readjust the brakes occasionally, they can be kept at their best in the meantime without jacking the wheels.

First adjust the rear brakes until the operating arm has approximately $\frac{3}{16}$ in. movement before the brake is applied. This can be ascertained by inserting one hand between the tyre and the mudguard and pulling the brake cable forward. Then adjust both front brakes until they are hard on when the operating arms are in line with the axle. This can be determined by applying the operating arms by hand, but it is essential not to force the arms (B, Fig. 1379) excessively in application. When correctly adjusted the front brake operating levers have five or six times the movement of the rear

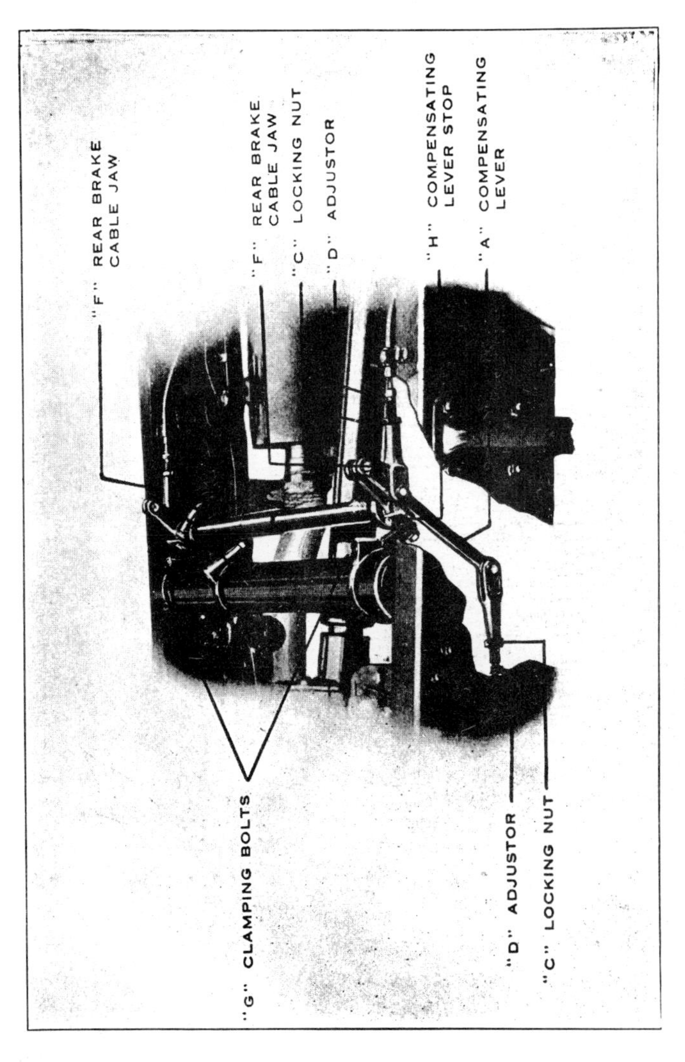

Fig. 1381.—Foot Brake Cross-Shaft.

ones. As a final check on the brake adjustment, the car should be driven slowly and the brakes applied heavily. If the steering is pulled over when the brakes are applied, slacken off the adjustment of the front brake on the side towards which the steering is pulled. One or two notches will be sufficient.

Never disturb brake cables unnecessarily, nor shorten to compensate for brake wear. The cables are very lightly loaded, and it is unlikely that any stretching will be encountered. If the settings have been disturbed and braking efficiency lost, proceed as follows :—

Adjustment is provided at the compensating lever end of

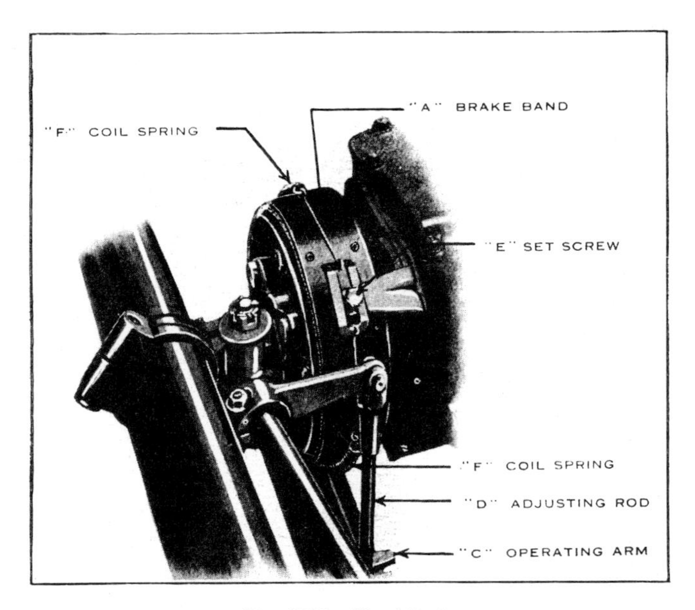

Fig. 1382.—Hand Brake.

each brake cable. Slacken off the brake cable adjustment locking nuts C and unscrew adjusters D. Hold each compensating lever A against its stop H and see that the top of each rear brake cable jaw F, when horizontal as shown (Fig. 1381), is level with the top of the frame. If not, slacken off bolts G clamping the cross-shaft bearing brackets to the cross-member. The shaft can then be raised or lowered until the cable jaws F are in the correct position.

Adjust the front brake cables until they just hold the compensating levers A lightly against the stops H. Then adjust the rear ones so that the cable slack is taken up, but

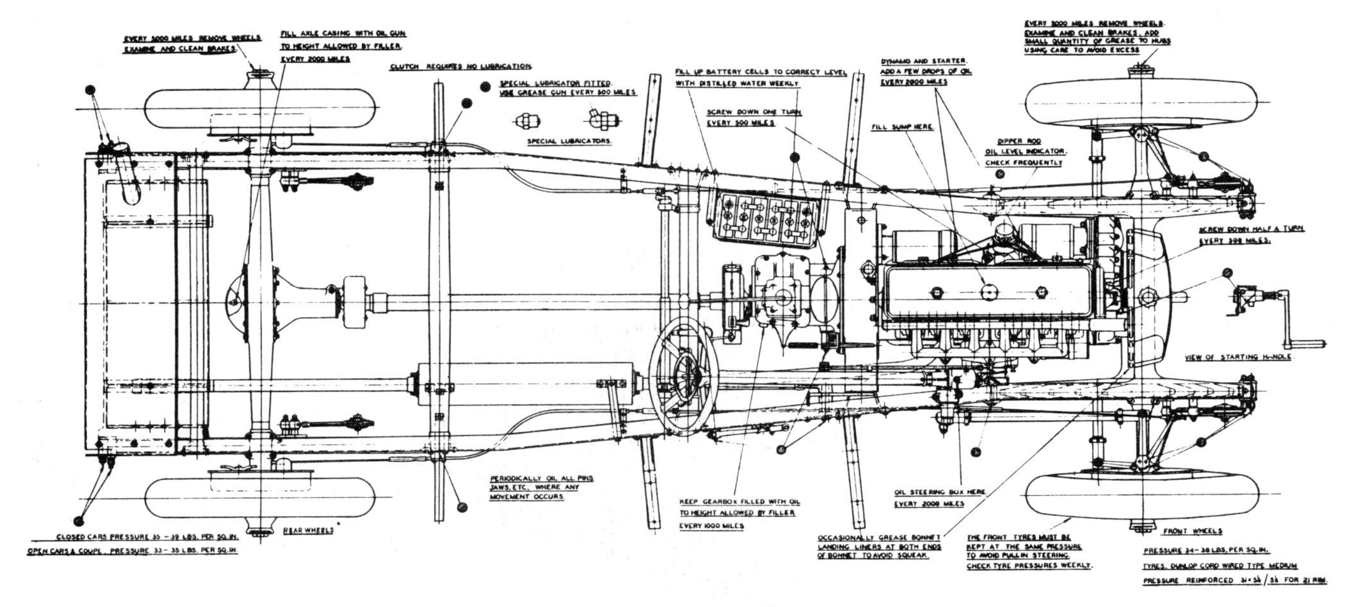

FIG. 1383.—Lubrication Chart.

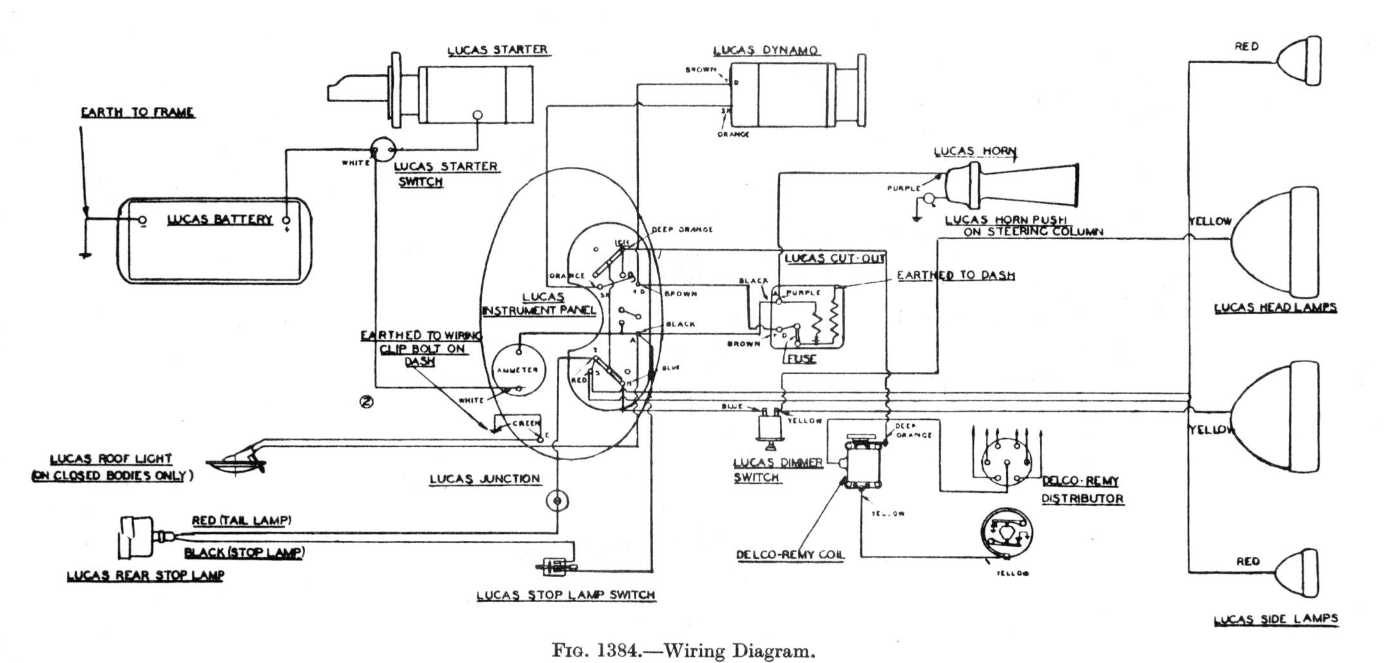

Fig. 1384.—Wiring Diagram.

not sufficiently to pull the compensating levers A away from the stops H. Tighten locking nuts C. Finally, readjust the four wheel brakes as set out above.

The hand brake (Fig. 1382) acts on the transmission and is only intended for parking use. An external contracting band operates on a drum mounted at rear of gear-box. Adjustment is made by slipping out the pin from the top of the vertical rod D and screwing down D one or two turns. A set-screw E carried on a bracket off the gear-box governs the amount of clearance between the brake band and drum, and should be adjusted so that there is a $\frac{3}{32}$ in. clearance between the set-screw and the external side of the band when the brake is on. Two auxiliary coil springs F maintain the band in the "off" position to prevent the possibility of rubbing.

The capacity of the crank-case for this Vauxhall 20-60 H.P. is $2\frac{1}{4}$ gals., the radiator $4\frac{1}{2}$ gals., and the petrol tank 14 gals. The piston clearance is ·0015 to ·002 in., and three rings are provided to each piston. A 12-volt lighting equipment is fitted, with a battery capacity of 56 amp.-hours and dynamo charging rate of 8 to 10 amps.

WOLSELEY

FOUR, SIX, AND EIGHT CYLINDER

WOLSELEY MOTORS (1927) LTD. of Birmingham give their patrons a wide choice of models, as they manufacture a four-cylinder, styled the 12-32 H.P., two six-cylinders, 16-45 H.P. and 21-60 H.P., and an eight-cylinder in line also styled a 21-60 H.P. In general features these chassis and engines are similar. Thus the tappet clearances when the engine is warm for both inlet and exhaust valves are ·003 in.; the valve timing is :—

Inlet opens .	9° after T.D.C., or 1 in.	measured on fly-wheel rim
Inlet closes .	31° after B.D.C., or $3\frac{3}{8}$ in.	,, ,, ,,
Exhaust opens .	43° before B.D.C., or $4\frac{11}{16}$ in.	,, ,, ,,
Exhaust closes .	7° after T.D.C., or $\frac{3}{4}$ in.	,, ,, ,,

and the oil pressures are 60 to 80 lbs. per square inch with engine running at road speed of 35 miles an hour, and 20 lbs. per square inch with engine idling for all models.

The order of firing of the cylinders of the four-cylinder model with a bore and stroke of 69·5 × 101 mm. (or 2·73 × 4 in.) is 1, 3, 4, 2; of the six-cylinder 65 × 101 mm. ($2\frac{9}{16}$ × 4 in.), 16-45 H.P., 1, 4, 2, 6, 3, 5; of the six-cylinder, 21-60 H.P., 75 × 101 mm. (2·95 × 4 in.), 1, 4, 2, 6, 3, 5; and of the straight eight-cylinder 65 × 101 mm. ($2\frac{9}{16}$ × 4 in.), 21-60 H.P., 1, 3, 7, 4, 8, 6, 2, 5. The piston clearance for the four-cylinder, the smaller six-cylinder, and the eight-cylinder is ·002 in. and three rings are provided. For the larger six-cylinder, however, the piston clearance is ·004 in. and three rings are fitted.

Ignition of the four-cylinder is by Lucas GJ4 magneto with 30° hand advance and no automatic advance, of the two six-cylinder models by Lucas GJ6 magneto with 20° hand and 30° automatic advance, making a total maximum ignition advance of 50°. Lucas or Delco-Remy coil ignition is, however, fitted on the straight eight with hand advance of 10° and automatic advance of 8°, making a total maximum ignition advance of 18° for this model. The contact points

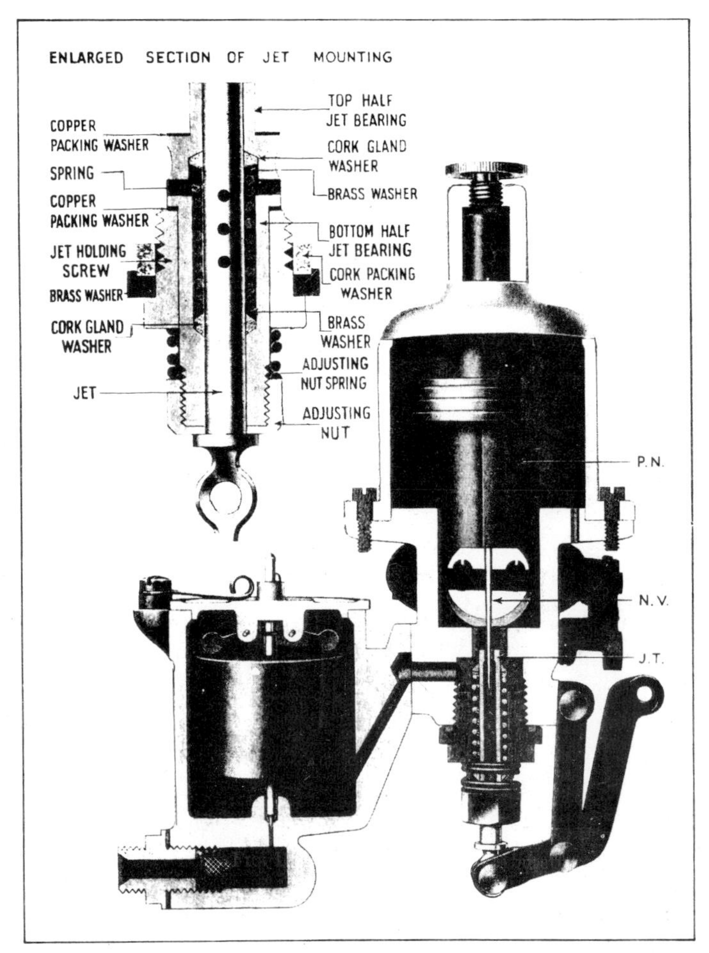

Fig. 1399.—Sectional View of S.U. Carburettor.

gap of the three smaller models is ·012 in., whereas for the largest in the case of Delco ignition it is ·018 in. and Lucas ·015 in. An S.U. carburettor is fitted on all models, and care should be taken to adjust the position of the jet by the nut at the base of the carburettor to give even, slow running with hot engine. A Lucas 6-volt lighting set is fitted to the three smaller models with a 60 amp.-hour battery for the four-cylinder and an 88 amp.-hour battery for the two six-cylinders, with a dynamo charging rate for all three of 8 to 10 amps. On the eight-cylinder a 12-volt Lucas lighting set with a battery of 63 amp.-hours is fitted, with a dynamo charging rate of 8 amps.

The capacities are as under :—

	Crank-Case.	Radiator.	Petrol Tank.
Four-cylinder, 12-32 H.P. .	6 pints	$4\frac{1}{4}$ gals.	10 gals.
Six-cylinder, 16-45 H.P. .	10 ,,	$5\frac{1}{2}$,,	10 ,,
Six-cylinder, 21-60 H.P. .	10 ,,	$5\frac{1}{2}$,,	14 ,,
Eight-cylinder, 21-60 H.P. .	15 ,,	6 ,,	14 ,,

The clutch is of the single dry plate type, having a light, steel-driven member, which is gripped between two fabric facings. The clutch itself does not require any lubrication, but a greaser is provided for the thrust bearing. This connection projects through the cover of the clutch and fly-wheel housing. Oil holes are provided in the clutch pedal bearings, access to which is obtained by removing cover from fly-wheel housing. The adjustment of the three clutch operating levers A (Fig. 1400) in relation to the bearing housing B should be checked from time to time. Lack of attention at this point causes the clutch to slip and the fabric will then be rapidly worn away. The clearance C between the ends of the levers and the face of the bearing housing gradually becomes less as the clutch fabric wears away, and it is very important to see that the clearance referred to is never allowed to become less than $\frac{1}{32}$ in. If the clearance is less than $\frac{1}{32}$ in., the three clutch operating levers A must be adjusted by means of the screws D, which should be screwed outwards after loosening the lock-nuts E. The clearance should not be made more than $\frac{1}{8}$ in., and great care should be taken to see that all three levers have the same clearance. After checking carefully with the gauge, lock the screws with the lock-nut after adjustment and again check the clearance;

$\frac{1}{16}$ in. minimum gap between the clutch release and end of clutch levers is the usual adjustment.

The steering gear is the worm and wheel type, end play in

Fig. 1400.—Sectional View of Clutch.

the steering column being eliminated by loosening the locking bolt A and screwing up the bearing B (Fig. 1401). Do not screw this up too tight, but sufficient to take out the end play, yet leaving the steering column free to rotate easily. One-third of the teeth of the worm wheel are used in the ordinary steering positions; there are, therefore, two-thirds of the teeth left for adjustment for wear. If there is any appreciable end movement of the worm wheel shaft D, this can be eliminated by adjustment of the thrust screw F. To use a new third of the worm wheel, if the back lash is excessive, take out centre screw G, loosen the clamping bolt H, and withdraw the steering lever C from the shaft. Turn the steering wheel three complete turns and then replace the

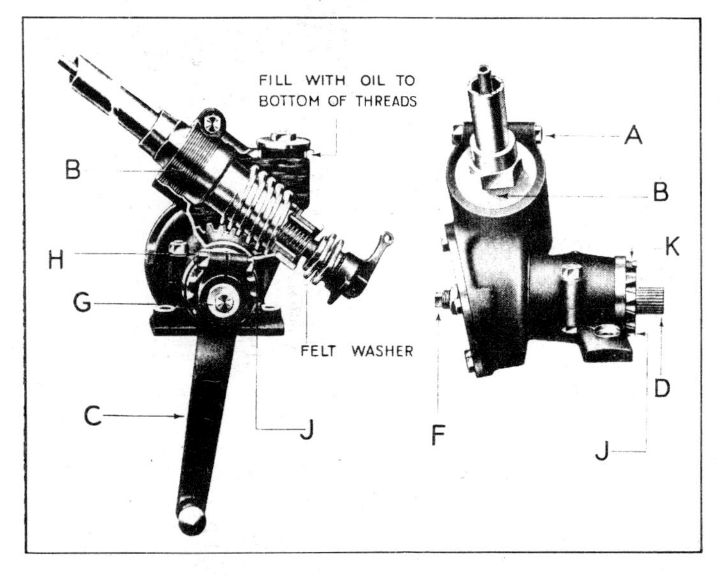

FIG. 1401.—Sectional View of Steering Column.

steering lever. The back lash will now in all probability be about $\frac{1}{2}$ in. at the rim of the steering wheel, which is the correct amount. If it is more than this it may be reduced by adjustment of the eccentric sleeve J, which carries the worm wheel shaft. To do this, take out the screw K by turning the sleeve J; the worm wheel can be made to enter more deeply into mesh with the worm until all excessive back lash is eliminated. It may not be possible to replace the screw K in the same hole from which it was taken, but three holes are provided to give a fine adjustment and the most convenient one should be used.

The brake adjustment is very simple, as there is a central adjustment for all four wheel brakes, which are the Alford

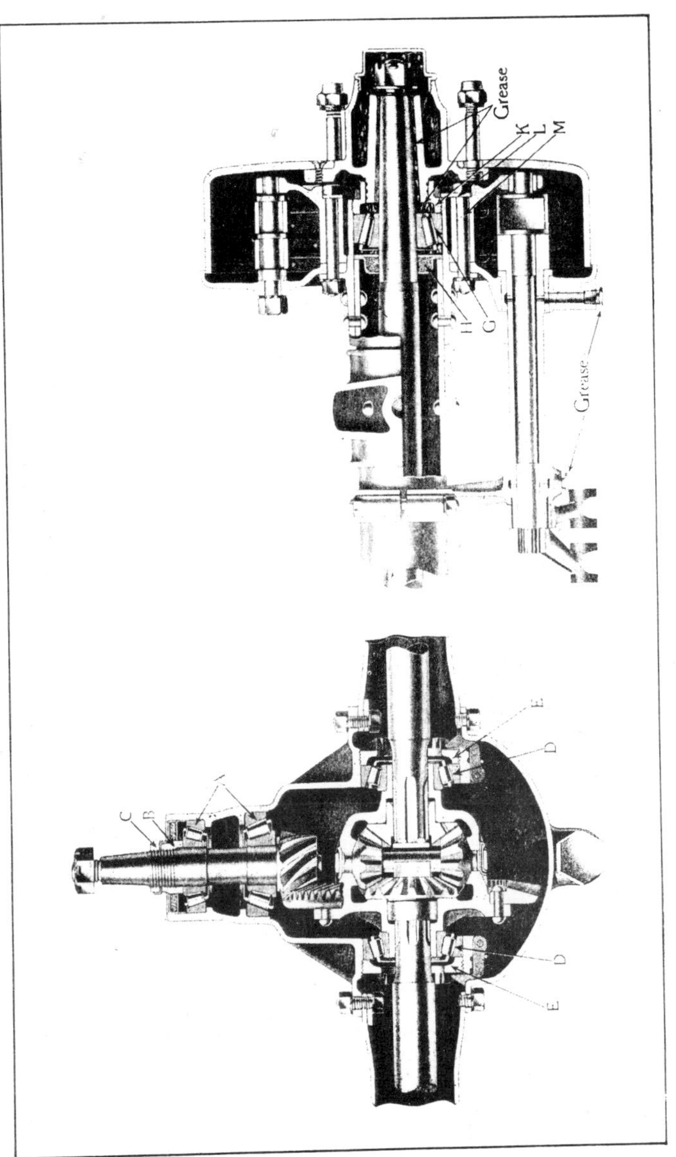

FIG. 1402.—Sectional View of Rear Axle.

and Alder type for the front wheels. Besides these, there are nuts at the end of the cables.

With regard to the rear axle and its adjustment, the pinion shaft and differential gear are mounted on Timken bearings, and there is an external adjustment to the pinion shaft bear-

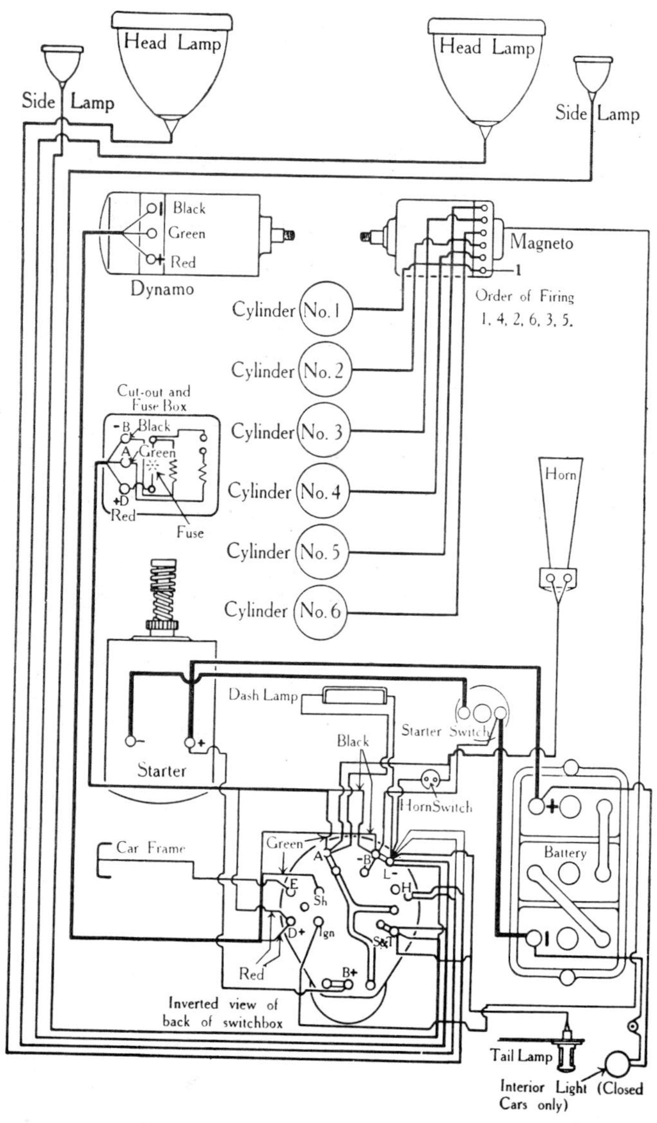

FIG. 1403.—Lucas Wiring Diagram.

ing and an internal adjustment for the differential bearing (see Fig. 1402).

The bearings A of the pinion are adjusted by means of the nut B, which is normally held fast by the lock-nut C. The bearings D of the crown wheel and differential gear are adjusted with the slotted nuts E, access to which is obtained by removal of the rear cover of the axle. Care must be taken that the endwise location of the crown wheel with relation to the pinion is not upset by unequal adjustment, or else the gears will become very noisy through being forced too far into or out of mesh. The correct amount of back-lash between the teeth and the gears is between $\frac{4}{1000}$ and $\frac{5}{1000}$ in. In the illustration G are the rear wheel bearings, not lubricated by the oil from the centre of the axle, owing to the interposition of an oil-retaining device H; the bearings are lubricated by the filling of the hub caps with filtrate solidified oil and screwing on, the grease passing along a channel as shown to reach the bearings. The rear wheel bearings are adjusted by nut K, which is normally locked by the washer L secured by the bolt M. It is necessary to remove the hub before adjustment can be made, by means of a hub withdrawer.

As the engine has overhead valves, care should be taken when making overhauls of the alignment of vertical drive for the camshaft, after removing the cylinder head for decarbonising, also to check the valve timing.